# The Other Side of the Pulpit

The Dreams and Screams of Pastors' Wives

## Elsa Siriano

5 Fold Media
Visit us at www.5foldmedia.com

God Bless!
Elsa M Siriano
Jeremiah 29:11

The Other Side of the Pulpit
Copyright © 2011 by Elsa Siriano

Published by 5 Fold Media, LLC
www.5foldmedia.com

Unless otherwise indicated, all Scripture quotations are taken from the Holy Bible, New Living Translation, copyright 1996, 2004. Used by permission of Tyndale House Publishers, Inc., Wheaton, Illinois 60189. All rights reserved.

Scriptures marked KJV are taken from the King James Version of the Bible.

ISBN: 978-0-9827980-6-5

# ENDORSEMENTS

---

*"Journaling through everyday situations can help release feelings unsaid. This is an essential part in our walk for trusting God. I highly recommend this book."*

Rev. Darla Edlin
Co-Pastor with Rev. Steven Edlin
Faith Temple Church, Rochester, NY


*"This book is a must-read full of humor; yet at the same time thought provoking, compassionate, and caring. It is written by someone who knows pastors' wives are human women although they are sometimes perceived as being perfect."*

Rev. Kathy Walker
Pastor/Evangelist with Rev. David Walker
Bible Missions Inc., Mt. Jackson, VA

# DEDICATION

To my husband David who believes in, loves, and encouraged me to write this book. Thanks "dear" for all your help with the computer (which I am still learning).

To my loving family, my son David and wife Glenda and their children, Karina Nicole, Andrea, Katherine Elizabeth, Karina Lynn and Alyssa.

To my daughter Darla and husband Steve Edlin and their children, Tyler, Kaci and Colin.

I love you all so much. You are the joy of my life.

# SPECIAL DEDICATION

———

To Karina Nicole, my granddaughter, who has
overcome many obstacles in spite of having cerebral
palsy. My heart broke when you were diagnosed. Your
story is written on the pages of my journals, a pastor's
wife on the other side of the pulpit.

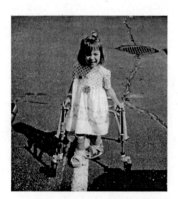
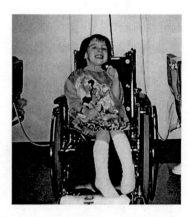

<u>Karina</u>
I can't run as fast as you can,
But I can make it if you hold my hand.

Maybe I'll fall if I go too fast,
But the memories of trying will last and last.

There are things some people didn't think I could do,
Yet I've done most of them and I'll do more, too.

See, I've got a family who believes in me,
Who say I can do and be anything I want to be.

I dance and sing and I ride my horse,
I have friends, a little sister, and my twin, of course.

I've had operations, braces, therapy and casts,
But the stander, walker, and wheelchairs won't last.

Because I am a fighter, so please take my hand,
And someday I'll run as fast as you can.

# ACKNOWLEDGMENTS

―――――――

Special thanks to all the wives of pastors. You all are inspirations for this book. Many thanks to all my friends and family who have encouraged me to write and endured the stories I've related to you. Thank you Kathy Walker for helping me fine tune my manuscript.

Most of all, thank you Lord Jesus for walking beside me and being my guide and best friend in this journey as a pastor's wife. You have taught me many lessons and sent me many blessings.

# CONTENTS

# PROLOGUE

---

It was a day of tragedy for some, the crash and burning of the Hindenburg in New Jersey. Somewhere in a small city in CT, a baby girl took her first breath. Death took the lives of many, yet several miles away the miracle of life took place. Did her mother know of the tragedy of the Hindenburg? Today we see events happening around the world almost immediately via TV and the Internet. Back then, news was broadcasted via radio. A news reporter cried unashamedly, watching people running for their lives while he broadcasted live. May 6, 1937; a day some would read about in history books and a day one little girl would always celebrate her birthday.

She always loved to write, read and draw. At an early age she drew pictures of her dreams; an ice skater, a teacher, a singer, an artist. In elementary school she wrote a story of children involved in a mystery, two of them being twins, meticulously describing even their hair color. Maybe she read too many Bobbsey Twins and Nancy Drew books.

As a child she sat in church, loving the music being played and the singing. At age 4, she sang a solo and as she sang, she held on to her dress, slowly gathering it in a wad in her hand, wondering why people in the audience were laughing.

Teen years in the 1950's started normally; school, church, home, and camp in the summer. Her friends, piano lessons, youth events, football games, and concerts became routine. Suddenly and without warning, her entire life fell apart. She arrived home from school to find a note on the piano from her mother, telling her family that she had left. Her sisters were at a neighbor's house crying. Her father stood by her at the piano, ready to console her. But her tears did not come and that was the day her heart turned to ice, anger boiling within her very soul. *This only happens to other people, not me,* she thought. No one would ever know she was affected by this loss. No one would ever pity her, was her determination and goal. She smiled and went on, with her heart broken inside. Her sisters went to live with their mother that summer but she insisted she would stay with her father and wait for them all to come home again, and restore the happy family she remembered.

Other women became her surrogate mothers. Other families became her fantasy home. Her best friends became her sisters. She clung to the hope of reconciliation in the family but she waited and hoped in vain; it never happened. She plunged into life with a promise, "this will never happen to me again. I will never again be rejected; I will never trust anyone completely or believe in true love."

So was the beginning of the life of a hurting child. Don't lecture her about divorce not hurting the children and don't teach her about a mother's true love. Don't try to persuade her that good always wins. However, the years carrying that hurt and anger inside did make her strong, yet along with the strength came weakness. It was indescribable pain that she tried to hide from everyone, even those closest to her.

Thus the journey began; one girl's life and the lonely paths she walked. Yet she was never alone because the God of her youth walked with her. Sometimes she felt Him and other times she felt He was far away, but He was always beside her. What you just read is the story about my life growing up. I'm sure I am kin to many who also walked in shoes similar to mine.

It was then I met her; the surrogate mother figure I needed. She was the sister of friends. She married young and had 2 children while still in her teens. I met her when I needed a mother so much. This girl was a family friend that took an interest in me. I eventually went South with her and her children. I left my father alone, not knowing where I was for three months. The journey went on for five years, meeting with and living with some of her family members. I watched this woman I admired go in and out of drug dependency, while having many relationships and marriages. I worked and watched her children. I became a "big sister," to them.

I thank God for the friends I made back then. I learned many lessons and grew up fast. Did I learn to trust again? Probably not fully, but in that family was a godly grandmother whom I admired and loved. But the journey did not end back there.

My course then took me several states away. I went back to my home and then on to college where I met my husband. This was just the beginning of a new and different life for me. I now belonged to someone and had my own family. I was so excited to begin a life of ministry beside my pastor husband. I wrote in his college yearbook, *I can't wait to serve God beside you and reach out to those God puts in our paths.* Our spirits were high as we repeated our wedding vows and began a new life together.

We would soon pastor a small church in the hills of New England. We had a bed, a couch, a table with four chairs, some lamps, and our personal belongings. We felt rich because we had each other. Our first child was born and the whole town gave me a baby shower, including a used crib and dresser. We were ecstatic and the world was wonderful. We were poor, yet would find boxes of groceries on our door steps many times. Our baby was showered with gifts from toys to a rocking chair and tricycle.

The church was in a large room in our house. The children sat in a miniature pew in the front row. They often ran to the bathroom just to flush the toilet, as many came from homes without indoor plumbing. Within a few years, we moved to another church and were blessed with another baby. Now our family was complete, a son, a daughter and a great church family.

It seems like people have many different ideas about their pastor and his family. After all, he is their shepherd, and leads them in their spiritual journey, preaching, teaching, marrying, burying, and counseling; just being there for them sometimes around the clock. I was learning as the years flew by.

The children's lives revolved around family, school, church and friends. We lived in a "goldfish bowl." Everyone seemed to know what was best for us, where we lived, what we should eat, how our children should behave, how we should dress, and so on.

We looked like the perfect ministry family when we arrived at a new church. We put our best foot forward, ready to meet the challenges ahead. But life is different on the other side of the pulpit. The masks come off and life becomes the reality of a typical family; living, loving, and surviving.

# INTRODUCTION

---

The following stories are the real thoughts, expressions, and actual events that happened to pastors' wives. You will experience the emotions and feelings from the other side of the pulpit. Names, places and events have been changed or altered to protect the innocent or the guilty. The stories are in the form of a page from the journals of many pastors' wives. Maybe when you read them you will understand your pastor's family more. If you are a pastor's wife, perhaps you'll see yourself and your feelings and not feel so alone.

*"That is why I am suffering here in prison. But I am not ashamed of it, for I know the one in whom I trust, and I am sure that he is able to guard what I have entrusted to him until the day of his return" (2 Timothy 1:12).*

# CHAPTER 1

# DREAMS

"Never be lazy, but work hard and serve the Lord enthusiastically.[a] 12 Rejoice in our confident hope. Be patient in trouble, and keep on praying." (Romans 12:11-12).

# 1

## DREAMS

---

*Emma Lou:*
    I want to sing. The choir is awesome, the music beautiful. Why does someone else always get picked for the solos and never me? I have a decent voice, I think. I was in the choir in high school and college and also in special groups. I love music. My husband and I sang together many times. Maybe the choir director thinks the pastor's wife shouldn't be given special attention. Maybe he has to ask the ones who have always done it. Oh well, here I am, dreaming again. Sometimes I think people look at me and expect great things of me because I am the pastor's wife. Then again, I imagine them saying, *who does she think she is, just because she is the pastor's wife*. I am having a pity party but at least I'm keeping it on paper and not complaining to anyone. Someday I'll read this journal and laugh and wonder why it bothered me so much. But for now, it feels good to write and get it off of my chest. Maybe I'll just sing in the shower.

*Alberta:*
    What a beautiful lady I've just had lunch with. She's known me from a child and now prays for me and my husband every day. Does she know how blessed we are to have such an intercessor in our lives? In the midst of stress, we feel her prayers. In the times of turmoil all we have to do is say "please pray," no questions asked, just prayers.

(Thank God for obedient prayer warriors. Tonight I need those prayers.) I am weary and tired of people telling me all the disturbing news of other people's sins and problems. As I grow older I want to be like Faith. She's my heroine and my shelter. *Thank You God for allowing us to have her in our lives.* As I lay my head on my pillow I am smiling.

## Elizabeth:

Inside of my soul there has always been a dream. As a child I wanted to be an ice skater. In college my heart soared to sing. Sure, there have been times I have been in music groups and even ice skated. Yet my soul still yearns to be somebody, to do something more. I want to jump out of my skin and be someone else. Who am I? I am a wife, a mother, a daughter, a sister, an aunt, a friend, yet the title that hangs over me is pastor's wife. I was so proud of this title when we first went into the ministry. Now it seems I hear it in my sleep: *Ask the pastor's wife; give it to the pastor's wife,* and so on. Then a note, a phone call, a handshake, a hug, and it seems those dreams that I had have all melted away like snow on a warm Spring day. The one "thank-you" is all it took. "Thank you for praying with me, thank you for believing in me, thank you for helping me when no one else would." These erase all the doubts I had about myself. What dream could match that? I cry, I laugh, I wonder, I question and I still dream. Dreams can wash away reality and reality can wash away dreams.

## Stella:

Today I looked into my mirror. What did I see? I saw a little girl. She has future dreams and hopes. She loves curls, frills, books, music, friends, and patent leather shoes. That was long ago and many miles have been walked. Many sunrises and sunsets have come and gone. Today I look into the mirror again and I see an older woman. Years have changed her looks and her life has been full. She has family, she has love. She has gone many places and met many people. As I look into the mirror I again see a little girl. She has more future dreams and hopes. She had curls, frills, patent leather shoes, books, music, and friends. She smiles at the looking glass and says, "Life has been good and life will be even better as I make more friends, read more books, have more music and buy another pair of patent leather shoes."

## Patricia:

I have been at the church all day in meetings. It's that time of year when every department re-establishes their summer schedule. Dinner is over; the kids are doing their homework. My husband is at a board meeting. I'm alone on the deck relaxing. It is evening, the air is still. Sounds are muffled. Far away music is playing. The smells of a grill waft by. The sky is still blue and the sun shines, giving its' last hour of light. In the distance a boat rushes down the river, heralding the days' lingering light. Birds call to each other, flying one more trip to my feeders. Their songs are all around me, each one a tone different from the other. The symphony of twilight; soon to be silent until the dawn of another day, when their songs become a harmony of life once again. Such sweet sounds. Life is precious, life is wonderful, and I am at peace and harmony with the sounds around me.

## Theresa:

My tulips have buds and are ready to bloom. The forsythias and daffodils are bright with color. Yellow, the color of spring. I believe God has the first flowers of spring be yellow to stir the dark of winter and replace it with sunshine for the new awakening. The forsythia bushes burst with yellow shouting, "spring is here, it's a new beginning." Then comes the bright yellow dandelions, shining through the green grass. Weeds? No, God's volunteer flowers. They are beds of yellow through the fields awakening our eyes to the beauty God sends us for free. Winter sleeps, and then the earth awakens with yellow, sunlight, smiles. God is in the seasons; resurrection, eternal life, His perfect plan.

## Yolanda:

It's nice to live in a parsonage, but sometimes I wish we owned our own home. Maybe someday we will. We have to ask if anything can be done and then see if it's in the yearly church budget. They take care of emergencies such as a broken furnace or water heater, but they forget that the parsonage speaks of the church in the neighborhood. The bushes are old and sparse from years of snow and wear. They should be pulled up and replaced. The kitchen cabinets are so worn and stained and the floor never looks clean because it is so badly damaged. I made a list and gave it to the board and they laughed and expect us to do the work even though we don't have the experience or tools to do it all. Most of their homes are updated, but they don't seem to care about the parsonage. I guess I seem to be picky but I want to be proud of God's house. It's really just a rent to us. Oh, I plant flowers and keep a clean home and yard. I do try to do my part. Some people live in huts and tents and we live in a house. I should be thankful. I hope no one sees me as an ungrateful pastor's wife. Living in a parsonage is a life-long sacrifice.

## Riley:

I stood in the hall tonight, outside of my children's rooms, thinking how much I love them. They are not only a part of me; they <u>are</u> me, for the next generation. I kiss my daughter and she smiles and sighs in her sleep. Then I step into my sons' room where I smile at their abandonment in sleep, almost as active in their sleep as they are in play; legs in motion, blankets half on the floor. I kiss them and they moan and flip onto their sides away from me. I pray that my children will grow up to know our love as parents and God's love for them. I pray that the ministry is a joy to them and that nothing negative from people will penetrate their souls.

---

When you were but a babe in arms,
I loved you.
When things were there to bring you harm,
I loved you.

Sometimes the way you choose to go
Will not be the plan for you;
Yet I'll walk beside you every day,
My love will see you through.

No truer love, no greater peace,
Than comes from God above;
He gives and gives and gives again,
There's no end to His love.

So take His love and give it
To those you meet each day;
To family, friends and strangers,
And you will hear God say, "I love you."

---

## Denise:

"I wish," "I'd like," "if only." These words have been in my thoughts lately. I wish I had more money to spend, more clothes, better hair. I'd like to have a bigger house, more time with my husband and longer vacations. If only I had more time alone. If only I could take back words I'd said without thinking. Tonight I ponder and think I'm too materialistic. I need to read God's Word not to see myself, but to see Jesus, who gave Himself for me. Here I am, sitting in a puddle of discontent. I should be sitting on a cloud of contentment for all God has given me; a wonderful husband, beautiful children, health, and so on. We all have our days of reflection, days of just doing the things expected of us. Tomorrow I hope to awaken with new visions and hopes. I will practice the little song I learned as a child, *Jesus and others and you, what a wonderful way to spell joy.* That's what I'm missing. The joy has become dim and I need to let the joy of the Lord be my strength. Okay, I'll stop rambling, check on the kids, kiss my sleeping husband, close my eyes and dream in joy.

## Christine:

If only church people would stay committed. Of course, many do. Then again, others commit to teach or do another job, and a few months later come back to us saying that God told them to do something else, or that this is not their ministry. Whatever happened to doing whatever can be of help to ease the burdens?

## Commitment

If we would all be faithful,
If we would give our best,
The pews would all be filled,
Then God would do the rest.

Souls now cry for answers,
As they search to become free.
Could it be you have the answer?
But you've said, "Oh Lord, not me."

I will not teach a class,
I will not fill a pew,
I have no time for service,
It cannot be me – it's YOU.
Someone else can take the time,
To listen to the cries.
I have too many things to do,
Too many errands and ties.

A still small voice then whispered,
My children what have you done.
I need you in my vineyard,
To help my kingdom come.

Make a new commitment,
To be involved in every way;
Come to every service,
Work, and sing and pray.

Show the world around you,
How much you love the Lord,
As you meet and worship together,
All in one accord.

# CHAPTER 2

# SCREAMS AND MASKS

"...God has said, I will never fail you. I will never abandon you. So we can say with confidence, 'The Lord is my helper, so I will have no fear. What can mere people do to me?'" (Hebrews 13:5-6)

# 2

# SCREAMS AND MASKS

---

**Sophie:**
Why God, why? She's so little and so sick. We serve you and pray for so many people and yet our prayers seem to fall on deaf ears when it comes to our own child. You gave her to us and we rejoiced and now You are taking her away. Can I really go through this journey I seem to be plunging into? People are so good to us but can they really understand what we're going through? We weep; we agonize and beg God for healing.

She's gone. I know she's in God's arms and yet my arms are now empty. My husband goes into the office and preaches on Sunday and midweek services. I try to be positive. I put on the smiling mask and try to say all the right things. Yet my heart is broken, and I can't even explain it to my husband. He seems so strong yet I know he's grieving too. I don't even want to feel happy. I want to lie down and die. I want to scream. I want to run. Please help me God.

**Judy:**
Today was sunny and warm. I weeded my flower beds and was watering when the phone rang. It was a church member and she had come from shopping. She and a friend had met for lunch in a quaint café. She then told me she had seen my husband there, eating with a woman she didn't recognize. I reassured her that he often meets with people to talk confidentially. She quickly answered that

she saw a certain look in their eyes as they chatted, hands touching. She felt that I should know, and then hung up. Oh God! Do I believe gossip? Who was that woman my husband was with? Can this really be happening? What if my phone caller is still calling and passing that information on? "Innocent until proven guilty" is the American way. I will believe the best. Why is my heart beating wildly, my stomach churning and my breath short? I feel like I'm dying. I hope I can report back later with a simple explanation.

## Molly:
"*O for a thousand tongues...,*"[1] goes the old hymn. Well, it seems a thousand tongues are wagging tonight. She wants to be involved yet when she is, she criticizes everyone and everything she possibly can. She seems so friendly and loving and I've taken it all in. Yet she thinks I am her friend because of her material possessions and that I'm jealous of her. How can she even think that? I have so many friends, some barely making ends meet and some that have an abundance. They are my friends and I love them all for who they are, not what they have or have not. True friendship surpasses all of that. Maybe she never knew true friendship. Maybe she's broken this friendship because she doesn't know how deep a bond that friends can have and she's afraid of it. She's left the church because of it; the blame will rest on those behind the pulpit. They will not remember all the people that have been hurt by her quick tongue. They will only think we did something to hurt her or her husband. Oh God, please heal her emotions and heal my broken heart. Help me to get beyond my emotions and feelings and forgive and love unconditionally once again. My first impulse is to never let myself get in this position again; never get close to or make another friend. I know that is my hurt talking but I am still human.

1. O For a Thousand Tongues, Charles Wesley, John B. Dykes, Public Domain.

## Pam:

It's all over the news, all in the evening papers. My husband, my pastor, my friend, has been involved with another woman in another state; a woman of ill repute. In fact he was caught by the police there. I want to die, I want to disappear. I lie here tonight, alone in my beautiful sanctuary, our bed, our home and I am completely devastated and full of anger. Oh, I smiled for the media, saying I forgive him. Even if I really do forgive him and try to make our marriage work, can I ever forget? What does God expect of me? Every time he holds me will I think of him holding her? Will he? Now I have choices. He seemed to forget our children and me and now he wants compassion and understanding. If I could just sleep tonight and pretend it's all a bad dream. Right now I am haunted, here in the dark, alone. I pray for God to give me strength and peace. It's a long road ahead for us and I want to do the right thing, for me, for our children, and for this man who I have given my life to. I gave it "until death do us part."

## Nellie:

She utterly stood up and screamed during the service last night. Our children were afraid and several people got up, to protect whomever she was near. My husband was preaching about Jesus and every time he mentioned that name, she screamed. That was just the second time I can actually say I observed demon power take over someone. The deacons ushered her out as she wanted no one to pray for her or to touch her. She threatened several things to the pastor and our family. Today, my husband went to our kid's school and signed a paper saying that only we, as their parents, were to ever pick them up at school. All I can say is, ministry sure is unpredictable. We live in a fish bowl and I pray it is never broken. I know God will protect us but I still have moments of fear and concern every once in awhile. I pray that this girl will want help to be delivered from this evil that probably is a consequence of the life of drugs that she has chosen.

## Fran:

The doctor said that my husband has only a few weeks to live. I can't sleep tonight. I can't really comprehend the doctor's words. Yes, at first I totally didn't accept it. I know his illness is not curable. I know no earthly medical help will extend his life. I do know his life is in God's hands and He has the first and last word. I plead to God, "He's too young, and we need more time together. His people need him, his children need him." I think back to the years after college and our burning desire to serve God and help people. I remember my husband's tears as he held our firstborn. Then later we stood with pride as each of our children graduated from high school. Our daughter's wedding was hard for him, as he handed her to her husband. Now she will bless us with our first grandchild. Oh God, let him live long enough to proudly hold that child in his arms. I go to church and smile but inside, I am broken. I hear voices saying, "She's so strong, she's handling this all so well." If they only knew the nights I lay awake and cry and agonize in my soul. I can't understand but I know I can trust in God to hold us together. Whether we have 30 years or 96, our lives here are for a reason. We must live our best, take one day at a time and cherish it, serving God and our fellow man.

## April:

As I look back on my journals, I see the same things have happened in every church we've pastored. I hear the same stories from other pastors' wives. Just when things are going well, and God is moving by His Spirit, the shaking begins. People all over, the same, only the places and faces change. That old devil puts his hands in and stirs up trouble. People try to take over and the chatter begins once again. Telephone calls to the parsonage with "she said," and "he did," and so on.

*Oh God break the bonds of evil, envy, discontent, fighting against authority and each other, bringing disunity. We've been in the ministry for over 30 years and we need to be lifted up once again. Please bring peace and unity to Your body, this church, and these people. How can this church rise up against evil when evil is rising up within? Give us strength God, to weather this storm. You are our Peace.*

## Michelle:

I am only in my twenties but feel like I've lived a lifetime in the last year as the youth pastor's wife. People complain because they think we have favorites in the youth group.  We pay attention to their child and someone else thinks we are neglecting the others. Sure, we take a youth out for lunch sometimes, but no one knows that this kid is coming away from the drug scene and wanting our help. The church kids have parents involved in their lives but some of the youth have dysfunctional families that don't care about them. After breaking many rules at the youth retreat, we sent a church kid home. We faced his angry parents who think we are incompetent because their child couldn't possibly be that bad. If their children do well, they thank us. If they stray from the Lord or the church, they blame us, saying we didn't do our job well enough. Will we ever please everyone? Probably not. All we want to do is reach this generation of youth before they are lost.

## Eileen:

Twice today, someone called to tell me, "I heard a rumor." When I hear that phrase, I wonder if they heard a rumor or are they nosey about someone or something and just want to know without seeming too obvious. Every church has them, yet I wonder if anyone ever confronts these busy bodies and deals with this problem. Maybe we ignore the problem, hoping it will go away but in reality it can be like a cancer and spread and destroy. If we pray, and truly want change, then we will work to make it happen. Tonight I pray for love and unity in our church. I pray for the rumor mills to stop running and be replaced with compassion and kindness and love. Dream on Eileen, dream on. Oh well, I can look at the positive and hope for the best.

## Mariah:

I often wondered how pastors' families cope after being voted out of a church, or being asked to leave. I remember years ago when a close friend was told he should move on, by the board of the church. It was devastating to the whole family. They eventually healed and went to another church, in which they learned to love and be loved again. Well, now it has been suggested to us that maybe it is time to move to another ministry. It sure surprises me how people think they know God's will for our lives even better than God Himself knows.

## Rosemarie:

I can't sleep so tonight I'll write. Inside are the burial grounds for the garbage that is dumped on us. As is with the old Indian burial grounds, forgotten, lost, then one day found when least expected; digging up the past that was once a future. I want to forever bury that past but some of it lives in a little secluded corner, just alive enough to revive when you don't want it to. *Oh God, take my heart and forever take out the hurts and replace them with your peace and love. I can't share the secrets that live within my heart except with You, God. Sweep me clean, melt the hard ice, and plant new blossoms. I want to bloom and live. I don't want to relive hurts and failures over and over. Am I human or am I just so mixed up that I can't let the past completely go?*

When the road seems dark
And the walk is bleak,
I cry to the Lord
And beg Him to speak.

I need to hear His voice so still,
Feel His love and care.
My ears are deaf, my eyes can't see,
It's as if He isn't there.

But wait, my heart is beating yet,
I've turned it off to all.
Then out of the darkness a voice is heard,
My name I hear Him call.

Don't be afraid of the storm that's come,
Don't listen to man's idle song.
They question and tear down the very soul,
Of a man that did no wrong.

I will avenge, I am in charge,
Of your life and will hold on to you,
Thus says the Lord to whom you belong,
Hold on, I'll see you through.

### Paula:

I sat in church today and I felt absolutely nothing. Oh, I know I should feel God's presence and I do know He was there, but I felt dead inside. What's wrong with me? Maybe I'm sick. Maybe I'm tired. Maybe I'm just sick and tired of church, people, problems, gossip, and phone calls. Help! I think I'll give up and run away. It would shatter my children's lives and my husband's ministry, but what about ME? I've read stories of women who did just that. They disappeared;

some for only a few days and some forever. I've heard of pastors' wives who left and took their children to begin a new life. I heard of one pastor's wife who left her husband and several children and completely changed her life. As I sit here and write, my heart is beating rapidly and my hand is shaking. If I leave, what will the ultimate consequences be? Would I forever regret my actions or would I savor a new life? If I stay will I come apart and not be an asset to anyone? Can I overcome this troublesome feeling? Am I heading into depression? Can anyone help me? Oh God, I need help!

## Anna:

It's dark, the rain is heavy and the wind knocks at our door. Our love affair with this church is over and blowing with the wind, washed away in a breath. The church board has taken control and wants a vote of confidence for the pastor. I know my husband and he will resign first. Only a few are the leaders of the march to oust the pastor, but is it worth an uproar of opinions that will only hurt the church? I am so scared! Where will we go? What will we do? *Please God, don't forsake us now.* Last night after church a lady came to me and said, "You are such a special woman and I love and admire you, but your husband leaves much to be desired." Wow! Doesn't she realize my husband and I are "one" and that was a hurtful thing to say? Who are the people that seek to destroy another person? Why can't they try to work together to come to a peaceful solution instead of having their own way? Perhaps their own lives are falling apart and the way they forget is to attack others.

## Kayla:

I've been to hell and back. It started a few weeks ago. I can hardly write about it now, still being stressed out, in grief and barely floating through each day. My husband was killed as he stood at the pulpit preaching God's Word.

How could God let this happen? I am so mad, at God, at the killer, at life itself. It's just not fair. How will I ever go on? I have two kids to bring up. How will I explain to them of God's love when their daddy was preaching about it when his life was snuffed out? Can I forgive as God does? No, I cannot; not ever, as far as I can see. Who is this monster whose life is so complicated that he thought that taking someone's life would ease his anger and pain? I am here alone tonight. The crowds of people have gone their way and the media finally is easing up. I am grieving my loss, but now I must make plans for our future. Where will I go, what will I do? Tomorrow will come too quickly.

## Jeri:

The board members called us and said they have driven by the parsonage and seen the lights on in the basement, late at night, wasting electricity. Of course, after a long day, with four children age six and under, I was up late doing the laundry (in the basement). Then one of the board members drives by on his way to work at 6:30 am to see if we are up or, as he puts it, "sleeping in." Then the word comes that the oil bill is too high and would we turn down the heat. We have babies, the house is old and not well insulated, so now what do we do? Tonight is a night I write down all my frustrations in hopes I'll feel better. My story is finally over, because last month my husband had an affair with a married woman in church. When I confronted him with my suspicions, he admitted it. I then found out he lied to some church people and now they tell me to leave him alone and stay away from him. So what do I do, with four little ones and no place to go? They blame me for the trouble my husband is in and say I am evil. I have a basement apartment, no job and feel helpless. I don't want to get my family involved but I may just have to call them. Where do these so-called Christians get the privilege of blinding their eyes to sin? *Oh God, please help me, I am desperate.*

*Gail:*

I haven't been feeling well and went for tests. Now I wait for them to come back and some more tests to be taken. In the meantime, the doctor said to take it easy, no work, just rest. I am fearful in anticipation. In my fear I feel both strength and weakness. My children love me and are concerned. My grandchildren love me even more than before. My husband's love and concern are overwhelming. Friends love and care for me. Everyone helps by stopping by with food. Doctors can be wrong and I hope that they are. In my anxiety I reach out to the Lord. I must relax in God's peace. How much can my husband really do, like vacuuming and frying an egg? In quietness, I look outside and see God's creation and nature. Patience is not easy but I must trust God. I must really rely on Jesus, my Savior, my Healer and my Friend. My life is in God's hands, I need not struggle. I believe everything has a purpose. I have confidence God will see me through.

# CHAPTER 3

## ABOVE IT ALL

"I am leaving you with a gift—peace of mind and heart. And the peace I give is a gift the world cannot give. So don't be troubled or afraid" (John 14:27).

# 3

## Above it All

---

**Margaret:**
Today was the worst day of my life. Our little foster child went back to his mother. But I love him. I taught him to walk, to sing, to say words, and to eat with a spoon. I potty-trained him and weaned him from the bottle. His mother gave up all these rights in exchange for alcohol and drugs. She has changed and gone through programs but how can I really be sure it won't happen again? Now she has him and my arms ache to hold him. Oh yes, I'll see him in church as the family attends here but it won't be the same. I know it was the right thing to do; to put him back with his biological family, but that doesn't erase the hurt in my heart. I pray that he will grow up to love God and have a good life. I knew this day would come but how can we ever be prepared to give so much love and then have to release it? I only pray that he remembers this family that loved him as their own.

**Elsa:**
Born for a reason, but just what is that reason? "The roads were icy," they tell me. Why did she have to be the only one killed in that accident? Our children grieve in their own way. My husband and I cry at night, uncontrollably and then when we least expect it, peace comes. Our foster daughter was so young and talented. Our church grieves with us as do her roommates and friends from the Bible

college she was attending. People have been dropping by with food, love, and comfort. We feel lifted up on angel's wings. What is the reason? We may never know but we rest in the fact that God alone has our lives in His hands. We still say "why" and cry. One card we received from a pastor and his wife, our dear friends, simply said, "We cried too." They are why we serve and why we feel waves of peace. These are the ones who hold up our hands. They are the reason we go on living and giving of our lives.

## Myrna:

I've had an interesting week. My husband is away at the national convention of our church. My daughter is back in college and I am here in this huge parsonage, alone. I am not usually afraid but this house makes strange noises at night. It reminds me of when we pastored a rural church years ago. The parsonage was an old farmhouse. The noises at night sounded like someone coming up the stairs. After many nights of waking my husband, he jumped out of bed and escorted me to each room, each closet and the attic to prove that no one was in the house. Yet this week, as I left for meetings, I left a light on in the living room so as not to come home to a dark house. Each night when I turned the key in the lock, I realized that the light was off. Was I imagining I had turned it on? After three nights, I finally stayed home, but I turned one light on and shut the others off, to see what would happen. About an hour later, a key turned in the lock and click, the light went off. I quickly turned a light on and peeked around the corner of the room I was in and there stood Deacon Ed, just ready to exit out the door. I asked him what he thought he was doing. With a smirk on his face, he replied, "Well, I was just doing my job, saving the church money. No need for lights on when no one's home." All I can say is being a pastor's wife sure is interesting and hardly ever boring. Time to stop writing and get some sleep and turn my light off before someone turns it off for me.

## Tammy:

How can I protect my children from the perils of being in a spot light and living in a glass bowl. I don't want them growing up thinking they have to be perfect or act perfectly. All eyes are on them. When they were small it was, "Oh how cute they are." Now when the teen age years approach it's, "Look at him, look at her. Her dress is too short, or he's fooling around writing notes during service." The other day our son said he heard two ladies talking and they pointed at him and said, "There goes the pastor's son. He looks just like his dad, maybe he'll be a preacher too." The day will come when he wants to be recognized for who he is. Our daughter said her Sunday school teacher introduced her to a helper as, "This is the pastor's daughter." She said to me, "Doesn't she know I have a name? It made me so upset." Well, in our home they are just our kids. We try to take them away from prying eyes and let them be just ordinary kids and I'm sure they appreciate that.

## Lynette:

I can't believe I actually said that! Maybe it was all a dream or a nightmare. There I was, in the midst of a group of chattering women. The conversation evolved in gossip about another church member. I turned to the women and said, "Whoever is without sin, cast the first stone." The conversation stopped immediately and all eyes were on me. Oh no, I thought, now what have I done? Well, slowly they all drifted away from me. I could see on their faces a look of shock as they discretely wandered off. I actually don't remember all who I saw in that circle but I think if they see me coming toward them in the future, they'll quickly go the other way. I hope the tale they were telling didn't grow as it traveled from person to person. It reminds me of *The Gossip* painting by Norman Rockwell. After traveling to many ears the information finally got back to the original person and she was in shock, as it was not the same information she had given. I guess the lesson is, "If you can't say something nice, don't say anything."

### The Stone
Go ahead, throw the stone
It will kill the awful sin
While you watch it land on its victim,
You can rejoice, because you win.

You've destroyed the one that wronged you.
You've trodden down the dirt.
You now feel so much better,
Finally, you've softened the hurt.

But it all didn't leave, did it?
The pain, the hurt, the fears.
They'll be with you forever;
Revenge won't wipe the tears.

That one stone now becomes many
That loosens on the way,
Because you threw the stone
But didn't stop to pray.

Please put your hand in my hand
I hear my Master say.
You'll find it soft and loving,
No stones in here today.

Lord help me to love and be loving
To the ones who hurt me so.
Help me to forgive like You do,
So I will live and grow.

Take my hand in your hand,
In Your steps walk each day,
And in Your love and compassion
Help me to always stay.

So take this stone I carry,
And crush it in Your hand.
Help me forgive as You did,
And help me understand.

Once You stood where I stand,
And You were tempted too;
But You gave Your life, You shed Your blood
For the ones who threw stones at You.

## Vivian:

*Shake us and send us the fire, Lord, like you did our fathers and forefathers. We need a God-sent revival, one that will not only shake us but will result in miracles of lives changed. This world is failing, with wars, drugs, greed and morals collapsing. They, we, need You, oh God. Help our church to be a lighthouse here in this area. So many people are quick to judge and slow to pray. They are quick to see faults and slow to be a solution. Help my husband to be so anointed that people will be healed and will connect to You. May the pew sitters get up and become workers, bringing in people who need You.*

## Esther:

She is only fifteen and needed to talk to someone. Her parents are both alcoholics and she spends her days baby-sitting her many siblings. I just can't understand such behavior in adults. Her dad slapped her because she was late getting home after a late music rehearsal at school. She knocked at our door, soaked from walking in the rain the few miles to our home. She sobbed as she told us her story. Her dad told her to get out. We said she could stay here with us. We called the police. They told us that they were aware of the family. They advised us that we could keep her with us as long as we sent her to school. Her parents had kept her out of school to baby-sit for weeks at a time. We sure never know what a day will bring. I hope she sees in us and our children what a caring, loving family can be. *Oh God, help us to love her and guide her in the plan You have for her.*

## Jane:

I think I'd like our church to be like the old churches of New England, where our forefathers used to faithfully attend. The pews were numbered or named and that's where your family sat. If you were absent, everyone knew it. If you were a visitor, you had a place also. It reminds me of a church we pastored years ago. There were a couple of visiting clergy to take part in the service that day. I was hostess to their wives. I looked around and finally saw a pew where we could sit together. As soon as we sat down, a lady came and said, "You can't sit there." I asked why and she answered, "My friends and I sit here and have been sitting here for the past ten years." Another lady hushed her up and led her away. I sure was embarrassed, to say the least, but after the service we all laughed about it. Well, we all have our place but maybe once in awhile we should change and reach out beyond our comfort zone. We may surprise ourselves and make new friends and have new adventures.

## Ruth:

Today in our quilting class we decided to make baby quilts for the Children's Hospital. This class is so diverse. There are a couple of women who only talk with each other in the class. They think they are socially unequal. Wow! Are they really Christians or just follow their family by religiously going to the same church? In the class, all are learning the basics of making a quilt. We take scraps of fabric, cut them into shapes, and sew them in a pattern. What seemed an impossible task then becomes a beautiful quilt. What a lesson! What were formally scraps and pieces of cloth becomes beauty when fitted together. People, like fabric, come in many shapes and colors. What beautiful harmony we'd make if we all would each fit in with each other, complimenting each other's gifts and talents. Maybe sewing these baby quilts will teach us all a lesson in love and unity.

*Phoebe:*

It's an interesting time to be living; Vietnam, protesters, drugs, Woodstock, and so on. This past weekend we had a music team come to our church. They were an interesting group. The girls were dressed in long dresses with scarves tied around their long hair, typical "Hippie – Jesus people" look. A girl came to our door Saturday night asking to borrow an iron. The odd thing was she kept her head down, not looking up while she was talking to me. Come to find out, the girls were taught not to look anyone in the eyes in case they would have lust in their minds. I must say, their music was fantastic and professional, to say the least. They appealed to the youth and college age, and also we who appreciate good music. Today our little daughter came to us and said, "You don't teach me right. I should wear long dresses and be holy." That did it. We sent the group off with a sigh, knowing they were influential in their subtle message, talking to people after the concert. Are they a cult that we should have recognized? Probably.

*Blair:*

Oh, tonight I miss my grandchildren. I see the families in church. I see the grandparents hugging their grandchildren and it makes me hungry for my own grandchildren. Being in the ministry, many times means your children will not live near you, and more so if they are in the ministry also.

---

### Grandchildren

I cannot hug you or kiss you good night;
Yet in my dreams I hold you tight.
The miles are many that keep us apart,
But miles can't take you out of my heart.
Remember no matter where you may go,
Your grandma loves you much more than you know.
The grandmother place in my heart is for you,
And will always be there whatever you do;
So when you close your eyes tonight,
Picture grandma singing and holding you tight.

---

Sometimes I call my grandchildren and tell them to look at the moon as I am, and it bonds us together. They get so excited that we are looking at the same moon at the same time.

## Ivy:

Today a friend died. She was killed in an auto accident. How I remember when we pastored the church her family attended. We two families did many things together and became very close. Then something unforeseen happened. She and her husband had some problems and she left her marriage and family. I was so shocked to learn that she would not accept counseling from anyone. She decided that this marriage, which had lasted many years, was no longer what she wanted. Everyone was devastated. We tried to talk to her but she refused any advice or help. After years of quite a few attractions, and a messed up life, we heard that she was back going to church and had straightened out her life. Now she is gone, after many wasted years, but home in Heaven. I wish I could fix all the people who we know are in trouble but miracle workers, we are not. My heart aches for all the hurting in this world who don't know where to turn. *God, help me to reach out and show Your love to anyone I come in contact with.*

## Rhonda:

It was a beautiful winter day. The sun shone on the snow, glistening like diamonds. Because it is December, today we were so excited to have a live Christmas show on our TV program. It went well. When the children's segment went on we had several children sitting on the floor listening to the Christmas story. Bill asked the kids if anyone knew what Noel meant. One little boy lay on the floor, his face in his little hands and said so innocently, "It means no water." How precious these kids are. It is so exciting to be a part of this television show. Sometimes I feel strange when I'm in a store and see someone staring at me. Some actually come up to me and ask if they saw me on TV. Our church is growing so quickly, it is almost unbelievable. With growth comes excitement but also new problems to face. Some people call the church office and want to talk to the pastor in a counseling session. The ones who are young girls come once and never come back when they find out I am sitting in on the sessions with females. Oh well, I have to keep my husband away from too much fame and idol worship. He is handsome but he's mine. Don't I sound possessive? Ha-ha.

## Rosalie:

They live in a house in the ghetto. From the outside I saw the paint peeling and the steps up to the porch needing repairs. The neighborhood was full of litter and unrepaired houses, some empty and boarded up. The family had invited us to dinner after church today. Our church is very multi-cultural, which makes it so interesting and a great place to bring up children in an atmosphere where prejudice melts away. We were about to have dinner with an African

American family. The moment we walked in the door, the flavor of the neighborhood disappeared. This house just shouted love and caring. The food was "out of this world" wonderful and I really ate too much. As I walked around the living room, I admired the photos of family members dating back to the Civil War era. I could see this family's pride in their heritage and I am proud to be their friend, their pastor's wife and sister in the Lord. God's eyes are color blind. His family is His family.

## Kailee:

It's so late and I'm so tired but I have to write while I still am shaking from the incident that happened earlier in the evening. Jane and I were on our way to a neighboring church where I was asked to play the piano because the pianist was ill. We stopped to get gas on the edge of a small town. There on the other side of the gas island was a familiar car. Before I even got out to pump my gas I saw Jim's face go white as he recognized us. Sitting in the passenger seat was a woman we both know, who immediately slipped down in the seat to hide. It was too late, as we had seen her and waved to Jim. He got into his car, stepped on the gas as he nodded to us and raced away. We were shaking for minutes afterwards. If she had just acknowledged our wave, instead of looking guilty, we wouldn't have thought something was suspicious. Our evening couldn't have gone by fast enough for us, we were so upset. We discussed it all in the hour's drive home. Six children in those families may be on the verge of a shake up, as well as the spouses. But we will remain silent and just pray for them all.

## Matilda:

Oh my goodness! I went with a group of women to a home prayer service today. If anyone that hasn't experienced our Pentecostal heritage reads this journal, they wouldn't understand. We are in the middle of a Holy Spirit movement in many denominations. Some call it the renewal. It is a wonderful blending experience with people who just want more of God. I have experienced it all of my life, being brought up in a Pentecostal church. We speak in tongues, called the baptism of the Holy Spirit as in the book of Acts, an experience not accepted as such by some evangelicals, but it is what it is. In this prayer service today, were some ladies who had just come back from a charismatic Catholic retreat weekend. The lady leading our group told of her weekend and then said, "Okay, everyone now sing in your prayer language." That alone was surprising to us as our prayer in tongues usually comes when we are praying and worshipping God and is spontaneous. Then she said, "Stop! You have to sing in your prayer language in harmony." Well, those of us from our church were at a loss, as we had never heard it put quite that way. I personally don't think God cares if we are in tune or not. I think our prayers and worshipping sounds like the best music to His ears no matter what tune or language. Some of these women had never talked to God from their heart and I pray that their new experiences give them a new personal relationship with Him who loves us so much.

## Monique:

April 12th -- I am so depressed. This has been a challenging few months. First, I was diagnosed with cancer. I just finished chemo and am free at last, of the shots and the cancer. Last night, my two daughters borrowed our car, stayed out late, and got into a fender bender. Church problems are now overwhelming me and I feel so alone in my dissatisfied life. What else is there? I have had such a sheltered life. Is there more out there? Can't sleep, so I'll search the internet to find something interesting.

April 15th -- Met an interesting couple through a chat room on the internet. They sure seem to understand where

I'm coming from and how I feel. Seems like I've known them forever. They seem so compassionate. They want to help me and meet me.

April 16th -- Okay, I've made up my mind. I am tired of this life. I want to fly, to go to another dimension, and taste what I've missed. I am totally packed and ready. My life is in suitcases hidden in the van, ready to fly away with me. My husband and children think I am going to help my mother for a few days, as she broke her arm in a fall. I am actually driving to the airport with a prepaid ticket waiting for me. Then, off to a new life in Canada with Annabelle and Jake, my new friends.

May 10th -- Wow! What a few weeks I've had. I am living in a beautiful home. I have a new car, access to as much money as I need, and new clothes. I have had many new experiences. I have gone overboard with smoking, wining and dining, yet it's not all that I expected. I am a good cook and keep this house very clean. These people have a few strange oddities, including suggesting some immoral activities. I called home today to let my family know that I'm okay. They've been sick with worry. So, I gave them a P.O. box to write to me but no address. I am not ready for that.

May 20th -- My husband writes to me daily. He reminds me of how God brought us together. He says that he will always love me, no matter what I've done and to please come home. I told him I want a divorce. He doesn't discuss that at all; he only reminds me of the good times and how much he loves me and prays for me. So now what do I do with two lives tugging at me?

June 15th -- Now I have come to a place where I am so far from God, so far from reality, living in a world I don't belong in. Today I picked up a CD from my suitcase and played it in the car. All of a sudden the words pierced my soul, as I heard, "Open my eyes, Lord." The tears flowed and I knew I must make a phone call.

June 20th -- I made the call and bought my husband a plane ticket to come and drive me back home. I have lots of regrets and must earn my family's trust and respect, but I am home, where I belong. I know that I'll read these pages in my journal some day and wonder how it all happened. I will always thank God for protecting and loving me.

## Julia:

We had faith that he would be healed. Now, after years of stepping through obstacles of disease, we saw him fly into the arms of Jesus. Tonight his bed is empty and I lie here remembering the many journeys that we walked through together. There were times of tears and times of laughter. There were times of need and times of plenty. We saw miracles of healing and stood by the gravesides of children. We were loved and unloved. We married young couples and lived to marry their children. It's been a wonderful journey of walking with God and knowing He walked beside us. Now I walk this journey alone. Some days are full of friends and fellowship. Some days I am alone and grieve for the touch of my life's partner, my loving husband. We were one as we walked together. Now as I reach out to him, my arms are empty. Yet, in the quietness, I feel his love and then I feel God's hand gently taking my hand, as once again I continue the journey.

## Joanna:

I was doing the breakfast dishes when the phone rang. "Turn on the TV," my husband cried and hung up. Our guests and I ran into the living room and saw hell right before our eyes. A plane had crashed into the twin tower in NYC and as we were waiting to see what had happened and why, another plane emerged into view and into the second tower it went, smoke and flames ascending into a beautiful Fall sky. Unbelievable events took place and watching it, we could hardly breathe. Tears came into our eyes as we held hands and prayed. Such chaos I've never seen and hope I never will again. The screen was full of smoke, ashes, sirens, screams, people running and jumping, the towers falling. It was terror. We sat there all day, numb, as did the whole country. Did we dare move? I remember the next day driving all over town trying to buy American flags and everyone was sold out. We wanted the world to know how we love our country and that we will never forget Sept. 11, 2001.

Where does the hate come from in the hearts of terrorists, of men who kill? Did a loving mother cuddle that son and place kisses on his head, one day many years ago? Did she teach him to be fair, to be honest, and to love others? Did he ever look at a delicate flower and wonder at the beauty? Did he ever hold a baby in his arms and wonder at such a miracle of life? Did he ever feel love in his heart as he looked into a lover's eyes with trust? Did his life here seem so bad that a promise of a better life in death seem better? In our own country, man's love of power, self and a heart of hate compelled him to kill. People of color, innocent children in church, and those walking to school; their lives were destroyed. They burned crosses with masked faces. They hide in the mountains, make bombs, and teach their children to hate. We close our eyes to hate and hope it will go away. On Sept. 11, 2001 our eyes opened wide, as four planes with innocent men, women and children became victims of hate. In one split second, many lives were snuffed

out, for what? A god, the terrorist's god, whatever his
name is, rewards suicide, violence and killing innocent
people, for what reason? My God is a God of life, love and
hope. His love is greater than evil. We must teach our
children to follow His teachings. In the end, good will
prevail if only our country will turn back to God, the
God our forefathers believed in and worshipped. I write
all of this so my grandchildren and great-grandchildren
will read their history books and then see how someone
in their family felt at this time in history.

<u>Sept. 11, 2001</u>
The day was bright and sunny,
My heart was happy and free.
A cup of coffee, the sea air blowing,
Then the call, "Turn on the TV."

The terror, the horror, the plane in the tower,
The fire and smoke all around.
The second plane exploding before our eyes,
Then both towers crashed to the ground.

We can't do a thing, we can't move a muscle,
Am I still in bed with bad dreams?
The sun is still shining; the sky is still blue,
Then came the cries and the screams.

"Oh God help us all," we prayed as we saw
The flames and the running crowd.
We gathered together, we felt their grief,
As we prayed for the victims aloud.

No prayer in the school didn't matter that day,
We were praying wherever we were.
In homes, cars, and businesses, in public places,
The thought of "no prayer" didn't occur.

One minute we cried as we saw death arise,
As our heroes rushed in to save.
But their lives too were taken, their families grieve,
As their heroes they put in the grave.

Do we understand as the days pass by?
How a person can be in such hate?
To give their lives and take innocents with them,
We must do something before it's too late.

We must rise in the fury and stand in our grief,
For all who will hold up our flag.
Our freedom was fought for and won many times,
God give us the courage they had.

So what is the answer, what can we do?
We ask of God, tell us please;
His answer is steadfast, His answer is sure,
We'll win the battle down on our knees.

# CHAPTER 4

# FEELINGS

"I know how to live on almost nothing or with everything. I have learned the secret of living in every situation, whether it is with a full stomach or empty, with plenty or little. For I can do everything through Christ, who gives me strength" (Phil. 4:12-13).

# 4

# FEELINGS

---

**Wanda:**

*Walk with me God, take my hand and lift me over the stones and ruts that want to trip me. You alone can see the hidden obstacles that I can't see. Even when I lose my footing, You are there with Your strong arms to gently lift me to my feet again. I feel Your love in every breath I take, in every step I walk. Please don't ever leave me. I can't walk in my own strength but I can walk many miles with You walking beside me, because You are my strength. So walk with me Lord, walk with me. Tonight I need you as never before.*

**Mona:**

Today I turned 60. Time stares us in the face and then slips away so quickly, we hardly realize we've lost it. There it is, there it was. I've lived 60 years. Oh, I want to go back. I want to hold those years a little longer, recapture more of the time I've wasted. What can I do to make the next ten years more profitable, more worthy? I could sleep more, dream and get lost in my dreams, but what would that accomplish? Self satisfaction sits inside of us and then goes to the grave, untouched and unseen by others. The face in the mirror is not me. It's only a shadow of the aging years. Who I am is inside of me, not growing old but growing in ways that can't be seen. So what do I look forward to? I will take the past years, wind them into today and walk into the future. I will carry memories and experiences for years to come, and write them into a life I will someday leave behind. I'll have more memories and experiences to share and new adventures to look forward to. I will take the yesterdays and weave them into the tomorrows so that those coming after me will hopefully cherish the today they have.

## Noel:

To lose one's place in life is like a balloon that escapes from a child's hand, and soars upward into oblivion. To find one's self in life is like a bottle that floats in the ocean and rolls with the waves up on the sand with a treasure inside and is found by an excited child. I've felt like both at some point in my life. I saw a child at the fair today watch as her balloon escaped and soon became only a dot in the sky. She cried uncontrollably until her parent diverted her attention with another one. If I soared away would I so soon be forgotten? Would I be so easily replaced? I hope there had been enough of me that people remember and sometimes smile with a memory I left behind. I hope some of me will live on in our children and grandchildren. Maybe they'll remember a story I told them or a song I sang to them, or a prayer I prayed over them. Maybe they'll look up at the sky with a smile and say, "Thank you."

## Margo:

Today went slowly, as I sat in solitude, my life before me, around me and behind me. Today is yesterday's tomorrow; tomorrow will soon be today. I am at a standstill, sitting and remembering. I will stand and walk into tomorrow, leaving today behind. I run, because I am free from yesterday. Free to step once again into the future of me. Actually, I'd better get going and cook dinner for a hungry family who is here in the present and doesn't want to wait until tomorrow to eat!

## Anastasia:

I sit here in my favorite chair and breathe a sigh of contentment.

> There is nothing like:
> The yellow of a dandelion in spring,
> The smell of a summer rose,
> The first smile of a baby,
> The laughter of children at play,
> The loving look of a mother,
> A father's approval,
> The sound of ocean waves,
> The smell of freshly baked bread,
> The hand of a friend,
> The blue of the sky,
> The sound of rain on the roof,
> The cry of a newborn,
> The first kiss,
> The color of a rainbow,
> The smell of summer rain,
> The prayer of a child.

I have experienced all of the above; I am blessed and my cup runs over.

## Nettie:

We visited a church on vacation and sat there as strangers. How nice to have someone shake our hands and welcome us. It was actually restful to sit on a pew, all of us together, singing and worshipping as part of a congregation. Because I play the piano in our church, I rarely get time to sing and don't even know the words to some songs. No expectations there that morning. We sure need this time once in awhile to just be one of the families, sitting together. For once, we were one of the first leaving the church, not having to stay until the last person left. I love the ministry, but sometimes need the feeling of being in the pew, on the other side of the pulpit.

## Savannah:

I have not written in this journal for several months. How hard it has been to "let go" of our two children and send them off to college as freshmen. My throat aches as I try to hold back the river of tears that want to flow from my eyes. I long for the children to burst through the door right now from elementary school, full of excitement with books, papers, and hungry tummies. Those precious days flew by so quickly. I want to go back and see our son catch the baseball in his little mitt while everyone cheers, or see our daughter sitting on the bench at her first piano recital, her feet dangling because she's so small. So this is the beginning of the "empty nest." Now I understand the sadness of my friends who have been here where I now am. Our children are at the threshold of their productive years. I pray their futures hold great adventures. Their rooms are still full of their memories; in pictures, posters, and collections. In a few years these too will disappear and it will be just my husband and me and a big empty house.

## Marissa:

Somehow, somewhere, sometime, there is some type of connection between us all. It's like a thin invisible string, stretched across time and space. Sometimes it's tangled and sometimes runs straight. The connection sings, cries, and lives on even though it seems to disappear. At times our lives are so complicated, yet we feel connected. To what, to whom, depends on the road we've taken. Our thoughts, our dreams, our aspirations, are all a part of us. Somewhere, we are a part of a thread that weaves through human kind. It's a thread of many colors, and much strength. It can be woven into many patterns and sizes.

It marches on, despite knots and frays. If we would just remind ourselves that we are a part of others, connected through time, then we can live together in harmony. I would like to take everyone in our church and weave them into a beautiful coverlet, each color complimenting the one beside it. One may be bright and one dull, yet the combination would be just awesome. I am such a dreamer, and then, maybe not. I'd better stop writing before I get too complicated.

## Marianne:

It's been a long journey and I am tired. What will I feel, being a new pastor's wife, just out of college and newly married? If I can just unpack before anyone comes to the parsonage to meet us. I want to be alone with my husband before he belongs to everyone else. *Oh, God, help me to be a good pastor's wife. I just want to serve You and do the right things. I am determined to look my best and have a smile on my face.* I wrote this a month ago. So much has happened. I began to teach a Sunday school class and one man refused to attend because he doesn't believe in women teaching the Bible to men. So he rides back and forth by the church until class is over. Unfortunately, as I stand in front of the class, I can see his car slowly passing by. The urge comes over me to shake him but I take a deep breath and greet him with a smile at the church door.

## Viola:

Today after church, I spoke to a woman who is grieving over her mother, who has Alzheimer's disease. She is losing her short-term memory quickly. She thinks I can't understand what she's going through. I've been there and wrote this many years ago about my own mother, remembering my parent's divorce, remarriages, and then this awful disease.

## Mother Gone

I can't remember if you ever rocked me to sleep,
Or if you held me and comforted me when I was hurt,
Or if you kissed away my tears;
I can't remember praises or hugs.

I remember camps and picnics in the winter
on the living room floor,
And sliding down table leaves propped on chairs.
I remember trips to New York City,
Vacation Bible School, church programs,
And then you left.

Did you ever miss me?
Did you ever wish you were back
or that I was there with you?
So many lonely years, so many questions I had,
none ever answered.
Now the memories are trapped in your mind.

Now it's too late to remember.
Now I come to you.
Now I look at you, a stranger to yourself and all of us.
Now from within my heart, in a hidden place,
Comes the love lost way back then,
somewhere, some other time.

I look at you, the mother I never knew.
I find love and I cry,
For times gone by,
And mother gone.

*Fiona:*

Okay, here I am again, pen in hand. It's a new day and I told myself I would only write happy things in my journal. I *am* happy. I have a wonderful husband, beautiful healthy children, and we are blessed. Then I heard that some of the older ladies in our church are bent out of shape because they call me and I don't answer their phone calls. They think that I only have time for the younger ladies, my age. The trouble is the computer.

I answer important emails and have the prayer chain on email. For one thing it is faster. Another is that the older ladies don't realize that when the prayer chain was via phone, it quickly became a gossip line. Only the prayer request was supposed to be given and maybe prayer together before passing it on, but it became a discussion time lasting for many minutes for some. I feel for those who aren't computer savvy because this is the age of electronics. I encouraged them to call the church with their requests or comments. I have received so many calls that were ending up just complaints. I have put the phone down and just cried because I just couldn't take it anymore. Why is it that people think that I am a sponge, with everything ready to soak in and not leak? Obviously, they don't realize that I too have feelings.

*Alicia:*

My husband, you are beautiful, as a man can be to his wife. I kiss your arm as you rest, glad that this busy day is over and you are relaxed in sleep. I touch you, because that touch is still special to me, after 18 years of marriage. You are mine. We've been through our wildernesses but are enjoying the fruit of Canaan that God has given us. It is so much more plentiful and sweeter than we've ever known before. This is what true marriage and love is. We are knit together, physically, mentally and spiritually. Never would I trade our relationship for anything offered in this world. You, my husband, are my strength, breath, and my life. I thank God for the plan He mapped out for us. We have taken a few detours, but the road is repaired and the journey is smooth. Again, Jesus is our strength. *Thank you God for us.*

## Blanche:

What a beautiful fall day today was. We went for a ride up into the Vermont mountains. I'm so happy to live in this beautiful state. I am reminded of Psalm 121:1, "I lift up my eyes to the hills—where does my help come from?" On our ride today, I was reminded of God's beautiful plan for our lives. He brings us through the Winter cold and darkness, and into the awakening of Spring; warm breezes, rain, new growth, and green grass. Then comes Summer; the sun, flowers and trees blooming, vacations, the water, and picnics. After, comes Fall again with a burst of color, cool nights, fireplaces, the last of the roadside stands full of fresh vegetables. Then once again we feel the cold, the snow, the ice and heavy clothing. It is so much like the churches. God seems to favor us with great revivals, and ingathering of people. Then without warning, come the troubles, the darkness, and the problems. If we would only wait it out and be there when once again spring comes and we again are refreshed. It saddens me when people leave the church when she goes through times of trouble and only want a time of celebration. *God, help us to be faithful and hold up the pastor's arms until once again we walk in victory.*

## Greta:

I write in this journal when I'm sad and sometimes about happy things or events. I write, so someday I can remember. I write to vent my feelings. I write about things I can't talk about to anyone. I write about things that bother me and things I learn. I write prayers to God and ask Him to help me. I write because I can. Maybe someday I'll read all the pages and see growth, or see the frustrations and blessings of the ministry. I'll see how God has always been faithful. I am alive now but someday when I'm gone and my family finds these journals, will they see a troubled woman or will they see a pastor's wife who triumphed over the negative and lived for the positive? I hope they see that no matter how hard the days are, God is always there, to lead, comfort, hold our hand, and walk with us.

# Chapter 5

# In Spite of it All

"...May you have the power to understand, as all God's people should, how wide, how long, how high, and how deep his love is. May you experience the love of Christ, though it is too great to understand fully. Then you will be made complete with all the fullness of life and power that comes from God" (Eph. 3:17-19).

# 5

## IN SPITE OF IT ALL

––––––––––

**Abby:**
    Oh my, we had a very interesting and scary day today. A person came into our office, which is in our home, fleeing from the Mafia. Ministry kicked in immediately and we led him to the Lord. The wife and mother of me feared for our family. Was someone following him? I pray that God's angels were around our house. I remembered one young woman and her small child coming for help a few months ago. Her husband had beaten her and she was covered with blood and bruises. We prayed with them and took them to a safe shelter. These are the stories that the church people can never know about. They think the pastor has a nine to five job or only works two days a week when he preaches. They should live in our house for a week. They'd hear the phone ring in the middle of the night and the pastor rushing to the hospital to pray for someone very ill. They'd hear the knock on the door after midnight and see a drunken person stumble in, who is confused and lost.

**Katherine:**
    Today I am distressed, to say the least. Our son stayed out all night partying. Oh yes, he called and said he was staying at a friend's house overnight. But when he came home this morning he went right to bed. Today is lady's Bible study and I have to leave him sleeping and

wait to have a talk with him. I will not share my concern
with the women. They will never know that there's turmoil
in the parsonage. I will be strong, yet why do I feel so
defeated? Haven't we taught him the ways of the Lord?
What's happening? How did we fail? Did we fail? When did
he grow up? Or is he grown up? Why did this happen when
my husband is away to a conference? So many questions
and I have no answers. I am simply drowning in self pity
when I should be trusting God for answers. I want to shake
this son, our first-born, who we dedicated to the Lord 16
years ago. Okay, I have a class to teach of women and they
have their own problems and concerns. We will get through
this incident. I just pray I will not over-react and push this
child away, but will use love and the wisdom of Job.

## Henrietta:

Is there anything so sad or so devastating as seeing
your child suffer? Our son's wife left him and now he
suffers, cries, and is in deep depression. His children
are gone, his life is shattered. Here we are, the parents,
suffering and crying with him. Our other children and
our church cries with us. Yet we go on and smile, trying
to help others. But in our home we shed many tears and
cry out to the Lord. Will I ever get through this? Will
I ever see my beautiful grandchildren more than once
a year? Oh God, we've served you and given our love
freely, yet our prayers seem to die before us. I lay down
to rest and sleep evades me. I am obsessed with sorrow
and grief. I know You will bring us through this terrible
time but I just wonder how You will do it. A whole family
is bearing this burden.

## Priscilla:

Somewhere in the shadows of my mind, I hear the
words of broken dreams, and a broken family, never to
be whole again. Only fragments, like glass blown apart.

I hear the agonizing prayers of children begging God to glue the pieces together. Did God not hear us? Is He wiping our tears?

Across the years she sat in a chair, tears streaming down her face. Somewhere in the darkness of her fading mind, she saw the scene and said, "I'm so sorry." Torment, dreams of what never was, regrets of what was, never to be replaced or bargained for. A child stands and looks back on a childhood robbed; a family broken and split apart. If only the two words, "I'm leaving" could have been replaced with, "I'm sorry." Many years ago hearts were broken. Now, another generation, other children and hearts are broken again!. How many pieces of me do I have left? Broken pieces are again scattered and lost.

## Grace:

Today we went to visit a family whose children attend our church. We are in a small community in the mountains, but I was not prepared for what I saw. Yes, I've only been a pastor's wife for a few months but I thought I had it pretty much under control. I am pregnant with our first child and still feeling queasy. We drove up to a house, unpainted, and a yard full of discarded, unwanted stuff. The door was open and the smells undecipherable. The children that knew us ran to us excitedly. The mother invited us in. On the floor was a baby bottle, half full of mold, with flies all over it. The baby crawled over to it and picked it up and drank, her eyes slowly closing, her diaper dirty and wet. Food uneaten was on the table and floor. My stomach churned and I knew I couldn't stay long. We told the mother that we missed the children at church and then we saw the attraction that kept them at home. There in the corner was the largest color TV that I have ever seen. We were sad as we traveled back to the parsonage. *Oh God help us love these precious people as You love them.*

## Roberta:

What a day! My husband called me to the office for what turned out to be a two hour counseling session. Much to my surprise, the couple was a young minister and his wife. They were having family problems which even reached into extended family members. As the conversation evolved, all of a sudden their voices got louder as they faced each other with different opinions. The secretary, in another room could hear them and told us later that she became concerned. I sat there in awe, watching two people crumbling before our eyes, yelling and crying. It seemed all their bottled-up emotions were spilling out there in the office. I thought, *what if there was no one to listen; what if their anger boiled over until it exploded and broke their relationship, family, ministry and church?* We talked, prayed and cried with them. Finally, a peace flowed into the room. We saw a slow transformation in the voices, eyes, and body language. They hugged each other and us and walked out smiling. We pray that they will continue to heal. We are humbled that God used us and that couple trusted in us enough to confide in us.

## Heidi:

What is my name, engineer's wife, doctor's wife, garbage man's wife, pastor's wife, or somebody's wife? I have a name. My parents chose it for me. I learned to spell it and print it as a child. If someone asked what my name was and didn't understand me, I'd spell it, making sure they heard it right. Sometimes I'm with my husband with a group of people and hear the introduction, "This is our pastor and his wife." Is my name too hard to remember or too easy to forget? I am mom to my children and "honey" to my husband. My close friends call me by my name. I am proud to be the pastor's wife, no doubt about that. I took his last name the day I married him and kept my first name, as we all do. Re-reading this, it seems like a small problem, a small request, but I sure wish people would remember my name and remember me as part of my husband, their pastor. I am a part of his ministry, yet I am still a woman with a purpose in life and a plan God has for me. My name is written in God's Book of Life. My name is on a line by itself.

## Agnes:

How can I handle people who lie to me? I actually caught a lady in a lie who supposedly is my friend. Was it to hurt me or to raise her own worth? I have seen people who lie so much and make it such a habit that they start believing their own lies. I have to forgive her and put on my smile, but my flesh wants to accuse her and expose her. Everyone looks to me to be the perfect pastor's wife who loves everyone, but I know that I'm really not. So, I sit here in my pity party and shake in anger. Then I hear a still small voice within my spirit, calming me down. I think of Jesus and His forgiveness and I know I will forgive my friend. I know I can once again love her through Jesus' love. *Oh God, help me be more like You. If I'm not, then I will drown in all the circumstances I face as "first lady" of the parsonage.*

## Dee:

Just back from a pastor's wife's retreat. What a great time! We played games, had a speaker, seminars, and ate. We heard each other's problems, prayed with each other, and had some pretty good laughs. One of the speakers was a pastor's wife. I have always thought she was the ultimate "first lady" of the parsonage. She looks classy and acts so aristocratic, and dresses so chic. She told a story of their early years as evangelists. They went to minister in a rural area, arriving late at night. They were shown to their room where they were guests in a large farmhouse. It was so dark outside and in the house as everyone had gone to bed. She had to use the bathroom but no one had shown them where it was. They assumed it probably was an outhouse, but didn't know where it was located. So, in desperation, her husband opened the window and held her out to empty her bladder into the dark night. Oh my, the laughter and disbelief of the pastors' wives just wouldn't stop, as no one could picture her in that situation. Now when I see her again, I will smile, because this idol of mine is really human.

### Verna:

Oh boy, did I ever have an embarrassing moment this evening. We had a local pastor, his wife and children attend our Sunday evening service. They have no evening service so wanted to visit ours. My husband knows him from the inter-faith ministers' meetings. I had never met them before. After the service a few of us stood around the piano, singing and fellowshipping. I was tired, after a long day, so I leaned onto my husband's shoulder and said, "Oh, I am so tired." A strange voice answered, "That's too bad." I could have dropped, when I realized this tall man with the black suit, who looked like my husband, was the other minister. Then when the evening was finally over, this family invited us to dinner at their house tomorrow night. I really do not want to go, because I'm still embarrassed. Oh well, I'll stick close to my husband. I bet that family went home tonight and had a good laugh, at my expense.

### Karin:

I just heard a saying today, which is very good to remember. Two things that will kill your soul are:
    1. Comparing yourself to others.
    2. Worrying about what others think.
I think I am guilty of letting both rule my life. I remember my mother always worrying about what people would say. She'd say don't do this or don't wear that because what other people would say or think of you. Sometimes when I go to

church I am aware of women's clothes and whether I look as good as them. Again I use others to compare whether I am looking or doing what they expect of me. It sure makes for a nervous fretful life. Then I am depressed if I don't measure up to my own expectations, or theirs. Whew! Guess I'd better start tomorrow by making it a point to remember that God made me to be me, a unique person, His handiwork. I should live every day to please Him, not others.

## Jane:

My family and I were traveling to minister at a church one day as guest speakers. Our two children normally travel with us. At the time my son was about six years old and my daughter was four. My son loves to find things around the house that he can creatively make toys out of; so it does not surprise me when he has empty toilet paper rolls around his wrists as armor, or a necklace strung out of paper clips. On this particular day when my husband (the evangelist) picked our son up from the children's church room, the teacher sternly told him to keep a better watch on what he brings into church to play with. Thinking the lady was just very strict with certain toys, he dismissed it and went on with greeting people after the service. When we got home my son excitedly showed me the cool jet pack he had made for his favorite stuffed animal moose that we had gotten for him at Niagara Falls a few years back. To my horror, "Moosie" had a tampon applicator strapped to his back with yarn! Even worse, my son had toted Moosie with him all over the church that morning! I can only imagine what the people at the church had been thinking.

## Sasha:

I met a pastor's wife today at the home of some friends of ours. She was so bubbly and full of life, so pert, so perfect in dress. Her hair was lovely and she was so nice to chat with. She had funny stories to tell us about her adventures, churches and people they'd met in many years of ministry. Someone asked if they had any children. Well, what a story she then shared with us. They had a daughter that had died from cancer in her 30's, and then a small grandchild died within the same year. You never know the life behind the smile or the tragedy behind the laughter. I do know that in telling us some of the story, she went on above the heartache and sorrow to pursue her dreams. Recently another one of her family died. I'm sure that she gets overwhelmed but leans on God to see her through, once again. I admire her, because she can smile and make others happy and has the personality to lift people's spirits. Whenever I feel down I will remember her and her sunshine smile, and think about her determination to live life as God gives her breath to breathe.

## Dina:

Tonight my husband came home after a long day and said, "I don't feel like being a pastor, or a dad, or a husband, or a boss anymore. I just want to be ME!" I know how he feels. He will change his mind by morning, I trust. If people would only realize the pressures and stresses of pastoring. Maybe then, they would be slower to run to him with every little complaint. One Sunday morning I had just arrived at church when a board member's wife came to me with six complaints in a matter of a few minutes. One was that there were too many extra rolls of toilet paper sitting on the back of each toilet in the lady's room and to her it looked too crowded. Seems to me that she wasn't prayed up for the morning service or else she had a bad night. I get tired of all the small chit chat and complaining. I'd rather agree together for healing to take place in people's lives. I'd rather sit at God's table and receive what He has prepared for me. What if that same lady had come in with an encouraging word and then went into the sanctuary and spent a few minutes in prayer for the service? Then the toilet paper rolls would still be sitting there and no one would care.

## Giselle:

When I think of God's goodness, I feel so small. I complain about such trivial problems, then God shows me His goodness. We arrived tonight from the Southwest, where my husband had several speaking engagements. The first place was in a large city. We landed at the airport where the pastor was supposed to meet us. We didn't see him, so called his home. His wife said, "He'll be there." So we waited and after an hour, called his home again. His wife said, "Don't worry, he'll be there." So we again waited and after another hour called his home. After his wife said, "He'll be there," I said, "Has he left yet?" Her answer was, "No, but he'll be there." "Never mind," I said, "we will be at the airport hotel." Around dinner time they picked us up at the hotel and took us to their house. They showed us where we would sleep. Oh my, the bathroom was filthy, the bedroom not much better, and there was a dirty sock lying on the bed. We told them thanks, but we would stay at the hotel since it was more convenient. The next church we went to, in a much smaller town, wasn't much better. The motel they put us in was absolutely filthy and smelled of mold. I sat on the lumpy bed and cried and said to my husband, "I just can't do this anymore. From now on I'll stay home." I probably don't mean it fully, but we'll see. There are so many good experiences, for which I am thankful. Some missionaries go through much worse circumstances but I think I am not so willing. *God, help me to see beyond the circumstances and look for what you want me to experience. Just please don't make it too hard.*

## Trudy:

Time flies and I love looking back on the many experiences we've been through. We are in a small village, which I love. The other night a couple got married in our living room. They had come by a few days earlier, with their license, and asked my husband to marry them on Friday night. They were just out of high school and she is pregnant. They knocked on the door about 6 p.m. with a few relatives accompanying them. No one was dressed up. Most had jeans and parkas on, as did the bride and groom. It was over in 15 minutes, but I pray it lasts for many years. This church is small, but the people are so loving and treat us like family. Some have very little education, but work hard. Who can blame the farmers nodding off in the service when they've worked since before dawn? They bless us with produce from their gardens, chickens, beef and maple syrup. *I love these people, God. Please bless them for blessing us.* They love God with their whole heart and trust Him with their lives.

### Hope:

Keeping up my journal writing has been a little hard for the past few months. We were so excited to welcome our little precious baby girl into the world. Her first smile brought so much joy to us. We noticed after a few months that she was behind in some things, and would often like sitting alone. After several doctor's visits, we learned that she has cerebral palsy, in a mild form, affecting her motor skills from the waist down. My first response was, "Are you sure?" That night I couldn't sleep. My heart was broken. Here we are, giving ourselves in ministry and now this. After learning all the things we can do to help her, it seemed that God spoke to my heart. He reminded me that now I have the privilege to reach out to other parents with special needs children. Other ministry families have children with special needs and we lift each other in prayer. I thank God for our precious "angel" He entrusted us with. She makes us stronger when we see her try her best at anything we teach her. I believe some day God will use her to help other children and bless them as she has blessed us.

# Chapter 6

# Help Me, I'm Falling!

"Share each other's burdens, and in this way obey the law of Christ. If you think you are too important to help someone, you are only fooling yourself" (Galatians 6:2-3).

# 6

# HELP ME, I'M FALLING!

---

**Sandra:**
    The phone rang just as the kids got on the school bus. My husband said, "You've got to come to the church office. A couple needs our help." Well, a storm was brewing in a family. The husband had come home in the early hours of the morning and confessed to his wife of 20 years that he had been having an affair. The guilt had overcome him, almost to the point of suicide. The wife wanted to immediately leave him. After much discussion she had been ready to forgive him, almost. She sat there in our office sobbing, "Our teenagers heard our conversation this morning and cried and begged us to go see the pastor and his wife, so here we are. What do we do now?" Inside myself I wanted to scream and hit that man and ask him why he'd risk his family for a few sinful nights of self pleasure. What was he thinking? Or was he thinking at all? Now he wants forgiveness and mercy. We are not God and it is a good thing that we are not for it is only God who can show such forgiveness and mercy. We will try to help them get to the place where they loved each other and work together on their relationship. It will be a long road ahead for this couple, but with God's love, forgiveness and mercy they will make it.

**Nancy:**
    I thought I had been in every type of counseling session. It was like a soap opera. There sat the husband,

the wife and the lover. Was this real or just a bad dream? He wondered why God let him love two women. He had disappeared for a few days and had taken his three little girls with him while his wife worked. His wife was desperate, and then there he was, admitting guilt and crying yet hanging on to the fact that he loved both. After several hours I felt like crawling away and hiding and let my husband handle it. Would this situation ever be resolved? *Oh God, where are you?* These people are members of our church and close friends. His lover has a husband and children. I feel like I'm in the Twilight Zone and that the end will be continued next week. My heart breaks for all of them. Maybe someone thinks my life as pastor's wife is so glamorous. If this is glamour then I think I don't like it. I believe God will restore these families but it will be a long journey. Lots of forgiveness and healing will have to take place.

## Louisa:

Okay, I've done all I can do. I've prayed, begged, fasted, been mad, and I have cried. I have been silent and heard no answer. Last week I was diagnosed with MS. The symptoms were mysterious at first, and then they became more obvious. I want to deny the words of the doctor, but I know I have to accept what's been dealt to me. I am miles away from my family. My husband stands by me and comforts me and assures me that we are in this together. We believe in healing and will keep believing that the impossible will become possible. The church will lift us up and be our family. Today in service they surrounded us with prayer, words of encouragement, and faith. *Thank you God for these caring people. I am your child. God, I trust in You, for healing, understanding, and love. Walk with me through this and teach me lessons. I can't do this alone. I need Your strength.*

## Candy:

Oh brother! This day has been amazing. The phone rang so early I thought it was still night. The voice wasn't familiar but it cried, "Help me, help me." I kept trying to recognize the caller and finally she said her name. A "long ago" friend was on the line crying because her ex-husband had died suddenly. He was the father of her children but she'd been divorced and remarried for many years. Was she crying because of her kids, regret, or what? I prayed for her and promised we'd be there for her and the children. *Oh God,* I prayed, *how can I do this?* How can we comfort her in front of her "now" husband? Why do people mess up their lives and live to regret it? Why can't they wait it out before they make big decisions about their future and the plans of their children? This is a hard situation to deal with and we face a week where we will need wisdom to minister to this sad and broken family.

## Ava:

I think too much. Here I am, writing my feelings. I watched the news tonight and saw a story about an unfaithful politician. His wife answered media questions, a positive attitude, but what is really behind that smiling face? I don't have her problem and I hope I will never be in her shoes. One thing I think I am guilty of is living my life behind my husband and his ministry. I guess I have not thought about who I really am, and what I can contribute to the ministry and myself. I remember that growing up I did have an inferiority complex. I never thought I was good enough for anything. Is this the life I'm supposed to be content with? I feel my husband is comfortable with the way things are, but deep in myself I feel unfulfilled. Am I anything without him? Do I have my own identity? We are one in marriage and I love him dearly, but I must find myself. Who am I? Can I find

myself and still be a part of my husband? I think too
much and maybe I should lay this journal down for
tonight and work on the questions tomorrow.

## Bertha:

Oh boy, here we go again. I am so tired, but before
I sleep, I must write. *Thank You God for this season of
snow, carols, excitement, good will and cheer.* We were at
the church all day. Today was the time when a group of us
decorate for Christmas. It is very interesting to see these
women and men all try to give their decoration opinions
without getting too opinionated. Every year it's the same
old thing. One lady thinks every wreath needs a huge
bow. Her husband got on the ladder to hang one and she
guided him from below with, "A little to the right, no to the
left, too high, no, too low." It was getting funny when her
husband almost fell off the ladder and yelled at her, "It's
staying where it is and if you don't like it then you can get
up here and hang it yourself!" Then came the discussion
of whether to have small lights on the window wreaths
this year. The lesson learned this year is, never have
just a group of people decorate the church, but have a
selective committee. As we were leaving the church, out
of the corner of my eye I saw another lady run back in.
I knew she had not forgotten something, but went back
in to change the number of poinsettias on the altar. She
didn't know I saw her slip out the side door and place
two of the plants in her car. What a day!

## Bonita:

Tonight I am remembering my mother. She was a
pastor's wife, and that made me a PK (preacher's kid).
She'd sit in the evening and tell us stories of before we
children were born. Being a pastor's wife, way back then,
was even more challenging than today, I think. She was
expected to accompany her husband to all meetings, yet

never enter in discussions or give her opinion. Her dress
was to be moderate in every way, including the hem line,
way below the knee. Wearing pants was not allowed, and
swimwear was out of the question. She'd sit on a blanket
at the beach, take off her shoes, put on her sun hat, and
arrange her skirt so her legs were covered while we ran
into the cool water. We set up our beach umbrella quite
a distance from other people. Heaven forbid should we
or our father see women in their skimpy bathing suits
that showed their ankles or knees. If they could see the
suits today they'd blindfold us, or as my mother used to
say about her parents, "They'd turn over in their graves."
We've come a long way, good or bad.

## Marisha:

Why do I feel so inferior to some pastors' wives? We
pastor a small church and I look forward to the retreats
for the pastors and wives. We have such a needed good
time with fellowship and wonderful speakers, great food,
and rest from the everyday commitments. One thing
that bothers me is those wives from the large churches.
Some even dress elegantly up in the mountain resorts.
To me, they seem to gravitate to each other, talking
about their smart children, large church functions, and
dramas. It's almost like a subtle bragging. Weren't they
once where we are now? I haven't bought a new dress
in over a year but they have the latest up-to-date chic
outfits. Can't they sit with us young wives and encourage
us? I cried in the elevator yesterday as I felt so alone.
Another young pastor's wife got in and saw my tears
and said, "I've been where you are now, but don't worry,
you'll get through this and be better for it." She made
sure I met new friends and I had a great time. I was
there for a refreshing and I did get it, along with many
new friends. *Thank you God for caring about me and for
sending people to bless me. Help me to see the needs in*

*others instead of seeing the material things I don't have
and don't need.*

## Janet:

Why do I feel so downhearted? Why can't I feel joy
anymore? I feel like a missing link that is lost and no one
can find it. Oh, I teach Sunday school and play the piano.
I teach the women's Bible study, yet I feel so empty. I go
through the motions of the day, getting the kids off to
school. I cook and clean the house, etc. yet I feel like I'm in
a dream, a puppet doing it all mechanically. Why doesn't
anyone ask me out to lunch or to go shopping. I need to
get away from my routine and interact with a friend. My
husband, the pastor, is so busy helping other people that
he has very little time for me. Somebody hear my cry.
Somebody help me find myself!

## Norma:

Now what do I do? My husband has been caught
with another woman. The church is grieving, our family
is devastated, and I don't know where to turn. This last
month has been full of changes. Sometimes I'd bury my
head in my hands and not want to face the day. I have
no money, no place to live and no job. I have my children
to care for. *How will I do this, God? Where are You?* I will
now have to make some decisions; grieving time is over
and I have to stand tall. I wanted to run, but to where?
My children need to see my faith in God in action. Their
father has disappointed them, removed himself from our
lives and brought devastation to the church family, to say
the least. I have to walk in faith, into a new journey in life.
I have choices to make. *Thank You God, for the people who
have helped us.* Some have come with food, money and
love. Some have taken the children to ball games, concerts,
and even bought them clothes. My self esteem is so low.
Yes, I've asked the question, "What did I do wrong?" I have

to quit being the victim and be the victor, so I can go on. *I need Your help God!*

## Serena:

I was just trying to help. Why did they turn my words around to make their story more believable? Now no one in that family wishes to talk to me. I really feel badly, as the lies came from their mouths and not mine. If I have to go to court, I refuse to lie. Truth is a freedom I take seriously. It's a commandment isn't it? Truth wins and lies bring a man down. Once lies become a natural thing to people, they begin to believe their own lies. The incident was over a child. Yes, the mother did take him to a bar late at night. She knew that social services would get involved. She was so high that her reasoning took flight and her appetite for drugs and alcohol superseded the safety of her son. I knew all that because she told me. So should I have lied when asked the question directly? I think not. I only feel badly that it ended up in today's newspaper and my name involved for all to see; the pastor's wife. Oh well, at least people in the church will see that my life is not as uncomplicated as they think. Now to sleep, as I try to take all the troubles of the day and leave them on the pages of this journal.

# Chapter 7

# I Give Thanks

"But thank God! He has made us his captives and continues to lead us along in Christ's triumphal procession. Now he uses us to spread the knowledge of Christ everywhere, like a sweet perfume" (2 Cor. 2:14).

# I Give Thanks

---

## Charlotte:

Easter, the Lord is risen! I saw several new faces in church today. Some heard via our radio program of the services and now several of them have given their lives to Christ on Resurrection Sunday. I looked around at the many families. One couple, Mr. & Mrs. Smith, both in their 80's, worshipping with glory on their faces, even though their only son was killed in Vietnam. Another family sat in front of them minus their baby who died during childbirth. Then another couple, so proud that their son is attending a fine college. There on the other side of the church sat the a faithful couple whose daughter and son-in-law are on the mission field in Africa. Next to them, a newly engaged couple who look forward to marriage and teaching positions. In front of them was a man who has been alone since his wife died of a sudden stroke, yet singing with his whole heart about the risen Lord. We are all family and worship God together. I smile as I thank God for being alive today and blessed with all these dear people.

## Betty:

When weeks pass and I don't take time to write in this journal, I have to catch up. So, here I am in my rocker by the window. The moon is bright, the stars twinkle, and my family is asleep. I love this quiet time to collect my thoughts. I am blessed. *O God, please don't let the phone ring or one of the kids wake up. I need this time alone with You.* I think back on the times I've felt alone, discouraged, rejected, or confused. Then after some time, here in my rocker, with only God to talk to, I feel peace, comfort and my strength is renewed. I look up at the sky and thank God for the good things in my life and realize that they outweigh the negative or hurtful things. *Thank you God for life, breath, a caring family, loving church people, providing our needs, and sometimes our wants.* I am reminded of a song our daughter sang in church when she was nine years old, *Thank you for the roses.* In other words, we have much to be thankful for every day of our lives.

## Regina:

I feel like today I've been in the twilight zone. Our son came home from college with a girl he wanted us to meet. He called and said, "She's the one, Mom and Dad. She's all I want in a girl. She's smart, sweet, talented, compassionate, godly, and I want her to be my wife." Oh we were so excited! They walked in and my heart did a flip. She is an African girl he met in a missions class. She is beautiful and smiled as she shook our hands. Over dinner, they chatted and casually remarked that after a year they would be going to Africa to work in a mission. Our only child, I thought, and they would be thousands of miles away, perhaps they will even have their children over there in that place. How can I be happy about that? I went upstairs for a few minutes to clear my head. My husband followed me and we sat on the bed together. He reminded me that when our son was born, we gave him to the Lord, to lead him in whatever the Lord's plan was for our son. We even used to pray for the mate he would one day choose. We prayed and went back downstairs. As I get ready to close my eyes in sleep tonight I remember a wonderful evening as we got acquainted with a wonderful girl who was soon to be our daughter-in-law. We fell in love with her and admired our son who was truly seeking God's will for his life.

## Carol:

It's raining. The drops are sweet and steady, making beautiful music on my window. They are like the tears we saw fall today at the funeral of a small child. How can we understand this loss? It's just not normal that one so young precedes us in death! But who are we that we can choose who lives and who dies? All I can say is that God is our Heavenly Father who knows all and will hold us in His arms. *Oh God, comfort that family. As the rain falls, Your love is constant and refreshing.* Today was a hard day to go through. Now I pause before sleep as I look at my resting family and feel grateful that they are all safe. *Be with that mother and father whose arms are empty tonight and I ask You to fill them with your comfort and love.*

## Eleanor:

Today a friend from many years past called me. I was so surprised to hear from her. We caught up on each other's lives. We had gone to camp together and kept in touch by letters and calls all through our teens. After college, with marriage and children, we lost touch. Now here we are, chatting as if years and miles never separated us. I felt so uplifted after we hung up, promising to keep in touch.

I walk along life's winding lane,
Sometimes in happiness, sometimes in pain.
It all is so much easier to bear,
When you have a friend to care.

The years go by; youth comes to an end;
Then there in the road, you see your friend.
Your heart is blessed, your spirit flies.
You know you're safe, in friendship's eyes.

No matter how bad the things you've been through,
A true friend is a blessing, always praying for you.
A comfort, a lighthouse, quiet haven of rest,
When God made us friends, His love made us the best.

## Celia:

Another Sunday, another day serving God, and helping people. *Oh God, how long can I smile and be the perfect pastor's wife?* Maybe I'm different, maybe I am not meant to be in this role. I am a mask ready to be revealed. *God, why do I feel so unfulfilled, so tired? I feel so helpless.* I love my husband but sometimes I feel like our daughter when she was four years old. She came to me and said, "Mommy, I wish daddy was a farmer. Then we could just live on a farm and run and play and run and play." That was when our parsonage was an apartment in back of the church and the only "play place" was on the sidewalk in front of the church. Tonight I feel like running, to be free; free from responsibilities and problems, free from people. Oh well, it's just a dream and I will awaken in the real world. I'll face the day and be thankful for the things I do have, like health, a beautiful family, food to eat and a roof over our heads.

## Amelia:

I just came home from a wonderful vacation. As I sat on the beach, I closed my eyes and drank in the sound of the waves. They are so constant, so soothing. The smell of the ocean breeze was intoxicating. I felt every care and burden roll off my tired body and wash away over the sand into the sea. Every shell I picked up was a gift from the sea. I had hundreds of them back home from many visits to the ocean but each one I pick up is new, another gift. Two weeks away have refreshed me and my spirit is uplifted. It is a time of cleansing, a time of renewal of who I am in God's eyes. I look inside and see the real me and I smile.

Yes, I am still here. Tonight I am home and ready to begin again. I know I can be what You want me to be Lord. With Your help I begin again to serve others.

## Mae:

As I lie here beside my husband, I listen to his breathing and I am thankful he's alive. Months ago I was sitting in the waiting room, my heart beating wildly as he was going through heart by-pass surgery. Our children were there and many prayers were said all day long. Thankfully, a nurse came out periodically to tell us things were going well. For the first few days after surgery I felt like a zombie just existing, going to the hospital and back. How I begged God for my husband's life and how I thank Him for his life. We've been through much together and look forward to many more years of exciting times, growing old together. Now I put my arm around my sleeping husband, my lover, my best friend and my heart is full. When the music stops and the church doors locked, here we are, alone, two people God brought together and I thank God. My cup runs over and over and over.

## Barbara:

What a surprise! I put the kids to bed, got into my nightgown and walked into my kitchen. There standing with my phone in his hand was a very tall man. "Oh God," my mouth spoke, "Who are you and what are you doing here?" He smiled and said, "I just came from the church and came in to use the phone." After he left at my suggestion, I locked the door. How strange these "hippy-type" people are. They come to church in bare feet, jeans or shorts, and nurse their babies in the pews. They talk about zero population, conservation, being free spirits and things we hear of in the 70's. They come because we accept them in the pattern Jesus gave us and I'm glad our church welcomes them.

Whenever I see them in their places of employment, their clothes are conservative and their hair is perfect. One night a week they sit on our living room floor, barefoot and cross legged, in total rapture as my husband teaches them of God's love. Their eyes light up and tears flow. I guess some of them are craving for acceptance and that love that is unconditional. Just like the old hymn, *Just as I Am*, they come; open hearted, accepting that love, so simple, so completely. I love this part of the ministry. I smile at the girl who has offered to help me plant a garden with all natural fertilizer; horse manure from her grandmother's farm. I know it will be an experience for both of us and I look forward to it. It will be two generations molded together in God's love, working with our hands and our hearts. This same girl has just come out of the drug scene, hitch-hiking across America searching for something that would satisfy all the empty spaces in her heart and life. She has found that something in a new life with God. She had many questions and that is why we are glad she has become a part of our church family, who have accepted her with open arms.

### Heather:

To give birth is truly the most wonderful miracle from God. All those years we prayed for a child and now, this week, God blessed us. As I look into my baby's eyes, I see the look of trust that immediately bonds us forever. I never really understood that love so pure, the love of being responsible for a child who would one day take my place in the world and carry on our family genes. *Thank you God, for this precious gift.* Our new names are Mommy and Daddy. We have entered into parenthood. So many gifts, flowers and food brought to us, overwhelming us. How can I ever thank these people, our church family who are blessing us? The times we give to them are being returned to us a hundred-fold.

**Penny:**

Tonight I am remembering the years we spent traveling, singing, and speaking. If I could talk to churches, I'd remind them of the times they forgot to tell us how to get to their church. Sometimes we'd arrive early and the church was locked and the pastor never arrived until five minutes before church began. We needed to set up for our music, so the service started late. Some pastors disappeared after the service, not even stopping to ask us if we'd like to go to eat with them. I'd like to thank the churches who were there to help us and took wonderful care of us. We were lonesome at times just for someone to chat with about ordinary things. It was a time of traveling and exciting ministry. I'm glad I can now know how our guests to our church would like to be treated. We know they like to let their hair down, laugh, and see the local sights, as well as share their ministry. We like to tell missionaries that they can call their family from our phone and they always appreciate it.

**Wanda:**

Finally, we have moved. We are closer to our children. It's only been a couple of months but we feel the pressures of pastoring lift and the stress level much less. I hope that as our last church welcomes a new pastor and family, they realize that they and the new family will go through changes. I hope they don't compare us to the new pastor, but let him use his vision for the church. May they be alert to the new family's needs and remember we are not super-human or unusually holy, but only people seeking God's will. I also felt called into ministry, as I stood beside my husband and fulfilled that call by teaching God's Word for many years. I feel fulfilled, but now what lies ahead in retirement? My husband gets called upon to preach but now I sit in a pew as just his wife. I smile again, as I do have the joy of the Lord in my heart.

When I was a child, I spoke like a child.
My dreams were childish dreams too,
Of faraway places, of castles and kings
And of sunshine and skies of blue.

Tucked away in my heart was a vision of love.
Someday my Prince Charming I'd find.
My life took some detours and cloudy days,
Around corners and up mountains I'd climb.

Out of the dreams of childhood
My prince did arrive.
First we were friends and classmates,
Then love blossomed alive.

Here we are, many years later,
Our love blossomed and grew,
Children, grandchildren we're blessed with,
Now back to just me and you.

My love for you is unending
I thank God for you every day.
Through good times and bad, sickness or health,
I'd have it no other way.

The love and the strength you give me,
I also give back to you.
I'll cherish and love you forever,
My husband, my best friend so true.

## Elaine:

Wow! In a age when things are changing so quickly, here we are, in a college town. There are thugs, Jesus people, and drugs all around us. Last night the local campus had streakers and, of course, the media was there in a flash – I can't believe I wrote that. Thank God for the Jesus people that came from out West, saying that God told them to come here. They meet in a house in the city. It's amazing how many of these kids are finding a peace in the midst of the scene of unrest. They need stability and love and are finding it in a relationship with Jesus. The drug scene quickly turns into a Bible study and lives are changed. This past weekend around fifty of them came to our church. They said that ours was the only church that accepted them as they are. I can't imagine Jesus turning anyone away. I can lay my head down tonight knowing peace. *Oh God, help us to always show Your love.*

## Angela:

Is winter over? Spring peeked her head around the corner today. Then she ran back behind a cloud, smiling, knowing she disappointed us but realizing she'd be back in a few weeks. Then she'll warm us and kiss the earth to coax the flowers to life, sing with the robins, nudging them to search out the best trees for their nests. We will all come out of our Winter cocoons to bask in the sun, stretching to the sky. I will smell the freshness of the earth and dance with the wind. Then the warmth of Summer will make us run with abandonment into long evenings and family vacations. The blazing entrance of Fall amazes me with many colors. Too soon again comes the chill of Winter winds, snow, and hibernation. God planned earthly seasons, and our lives also have seasons. Youth, awakening, we are aging into Winter. I think our churches are like that also; many seasons, transitions, highs and lows. I hope to survive them all.

## Leah:

Today was beautiful. We traveled to see our grandson dedicated in our son's church. What a beautiful service!

How wonderful to be a grandparent, reminiscing about
our own children's dedications. I was thinking about my
grandparents, some whom I never met. Two lived in
Europe. My mother's mother died when she was twenty-
three and my mother only two years old. My grandfather
died when I was five years old. I remember sitting on
his lap while he drew me pictures. He was a musician
and I thank him for that heritage. He passed his gift of
music down to many in his family. He composed, taught
lessons, and music was his life, as well as his work. So
many years later, music is a part of our lives also. Music
speaks to me. It can make me happy and also move
me to tears. When problems in church get me down, I
turn on the music and it soothes me. I can dance in my
kitchen, sing along, or just close my eyes and inhale the
beauty of a sacred Psalm calming my soul.

## Lynn:

This is an exciting life and I must write some things
in this journal so I can look back years later to remind
myself of how God took care of us. I complained because
our toddler outgrew last year's winter jacket and someone
gave him a beautiful snowsuit. It was the same day I was
complaining because we had no extra money to buy him
one. I cried because we had hardly any food. I opened the
door and there was a large box full of food someone had
dropped by. Our daughter needed shoes and a lady in
church brought her expensive shoes and clothes a wealthy
client's child had outgrown. The year we pioneered a new
church, someone paid for our daughter's piano lessons
and braces. Someone else bought our children's school
clothes. I sit here and thank God for always looking out
for us, always supplying our needs. I trust this all will help
our children to trust God in their lives. I will tell them the
stories of how our needs were met and I hope they'll tell
their children and their children's children.

## Chelsea:

Today we came home from a mission's trip to a Third World country. My mind is racing with all the memories I have stored there. Some people think we do not have a right to convince others to leave their old religious rites and ways to serve a God they have never heard of. Well, had they walked with us, they may have changed their minds. I saw men who would have killed for their sacrificial offerings to a god they believed in. When we brought them the message of God's love and of Jesus who died for their sins, these men bowed to the ground and wept. Their question was, "He loves me? Why? Why didn't someone tell us before now?" I saw our team pray for a woman on her death bed in a simple hut, arise, smile, and ask for food. All her relatives gathered around us and said, "Teach us to pray to this Jesus you tell us about." My heart swells and I pray for the day I can again share my Jesus with such hungry people. I feel privileged to have been there. Now back home in my own house I thank God for all He has given me.

## Marlena:

Do I believe in angels? Do I believe God sends messengers to us? I don't know if I did so much, but after today, well, it could be that I do. We were just ready to sit down for lunch. My husband came over from the church and the kids were already at the table when someone knocked at the door. There stood a man. He had a long beard, long hair and clothes that looked travel-worn. He said he had been walking and getting rides through many states, stopping at churches. My husband invited him to eat with us. It was apparent that he was very hungry. He kept us spellbound, as he told us of his travels. He said he wants to encourage ministers to keep preaching God's Word and not give up. He had a beautiful smile and soft manner. He thanked us for the meal and said that he must get going. As our house is right on the road, we can see in either direction, so I went to the window to see which way he went and saw no one. I called my husband to come look and it's as if this man disappeared into thin air. No matter which way he went, we would have seen him walking. As we were standing there in awe, our little girl said, "Mommy, Daddy, was that Jesus?" Well, today, I believe someone was sent to us, to encourage us, and we fed him. Or did He feed us?

## Beth:

I want to thank the women in my church who made today possible. I will send them some cards tomorrow. They gave me a surprise birthday luncheon last week, and one of the gifts was a semester of art lessons at a local college. Inside of me laid a buried dream, to capture on canvas, the beautiful mountains, quiet villages, stately trees, the sapphire sea, the autumn colors and the rolling hills. Today the door to that dream was opened. I sat in front of a canvas, oils and palette knife in my hands. A few minutes of instruction and then the quickening of my heart and breath, as I lifted my hand and put the first stroke of color on the canvas. The dream took a burst of flight and was free at last. Where will it take me? I will never be the same. My eyes close in sleep and before me are dancing colors, waiting to be tamed by me to take their place on the canvas. How can I wait until the next lesson?

## Ellie:

I woke up this morning with a song in my heart; *Jesus, I'm depending on You.* I depend on Him each day, to face whatever the day has ahead for me. Yesterday, our small daughter had a high fever. The doctor said that she has pneumonia. He would have put her in the hospital pediatric unit but so many children are there already with the same illness. They are sick but not so sick to stay bedridden and are running the nurses crazy. So, my job is to try and keep our energetic child calmed down. My job soon ended. We laid hands on her and prayed for healing. At the "amen," she jumped out of bed, running around the room screaming, "I'm healed! Jesus healed me and now I'm all better!" What could we say? The faith of a child is so pure and trusting. Thank God, she finally took a nap. Her temperature upon awakening was normal and her remark was sweet as she looked at me with a smile and said, "Mommy, I told you that Jesus healed me. Don't you believe me?"

# CHAPTER 8

# I REGRET, I REMEMBER

"As we pray to our God and Father about you, we think of your faithful work, your loving deeds, and the enduring hope you have because of our Lord Jesus Christ" (1 Thes. 1:3).

8

# I Regret, I Remember

---

*Sylvia:*
    A couple in our church is at the stage in their lives when they need to downsize. Their health makes it almost impossible to keep up with a large house. We visited them and saw the sadness as they told us their plans. It's hard to imagine their feelings completely because I'm still young and collecting my own memories. The time will come when our children might refuse our generous offer to own all the things we've kept for them down through the years. I know I'll be sad then but now I want to help this elderly couple to keep their most treasured keepsakes but gently let go of the unneeded collections. Their children live across country and only visit occasionally, so we have offered to help them.

Stuff
Don't throw all my "stuff" away,
Please don't even suggest that I do;
It's all in the boxes and drawers,
Waiting for me to go through.

I need to sort through and organize,
The pictures, the papers, covered with dust;
It may take a long time to do it,
But to reminisce and do it I must.

Each little drawing, each little note
Is a precious part of my past;
I smile as I look at mementos,
They're pieces of memories that last.

Here is a newspaper article,
Did it happen so long ago?
A box of trivial trinkets,
All treasured reminders, I know.

Please let me walk through the years,
I promise to be back again soon;
I'll start early in the morning,
And perhaps stop for lunch at noon.

Here's a picture of us at the circus,
And one of Smokey, our cat;
There're clothes the kids wore as babies,
Booties, tiny shoes and a hat.

See, the babies are grown, with babes of their own,
The years march on, oh so fast;
So I keep all the trinkets and things that I love,
As my visible link with the past.

Please don't throw all my "stuff" away,
I need to organize more;
Wait 'til I'm gone and can no longer see,
My precious memories tucked in a drawer.

*Olivia:*
I can't believe she escaped from prison today.
It wasn't long until she was caught and it was on
the local news. If only I had called her. I felt strongly
to call her earlier today but didn't. Then I turned
on the six o'clock news, and I experienced regret. It

reminds me of my dad, who years ago was awakened in the night by hearing a voice saying, "Go talk to John about Me, Jesus." Well, dad thought he couldn't because his English wasn't good, etc. In the morning he went to the bank and a group of men were talking excitedly. He asked what was wrong and one man said, "Early this morning, John hung himself." Each year my dad went to John's grave and said, "If only I had gone to you and told you about Jesus and how much He loves you." So, you can be sure that I will obey the voice within me from now on. If we show love and compassion to others, we build strength within ourselves. Tomorrow I will call my friend, in prison and tell her that I love her and Jesus loves her, I'll be praying for her and she will make it.

## Madison:

Finally, retirement day. No more board meetings, no more people's troubles and criticism. Now what? I'll miss the comfort of the church family, I'm sure. I'll miss the hugs of the children and my friends of the past twenty years in this church. We've seen marriages, births, funerals, graduations, and hospital stays. These are our family. They've walked with, prayed for, fed, loved, and blessed us with gifts. Now we are supposed to close the parsonage door and walk out of their lives. The old unspoken rule is to leave and give them to the next pastor. But I ask the question, how do you take a friendship of twenty years and just forget? I think when God brings special friends into our lives it is not just for a season every time. In our ministry in several churches we have a few families that have kept in touch through the years. Today as we sat at a table at our retirement celebration, surrounded by family, there were some of those "forever friends" along with the people of this church. I look forward to the next journey God will lead us on, with tears reminding me of the memories we leave behind.

## Renee:

Today was stormy and gray. I felt like pulling the blankets over my head and closing out the world. Then I'd emerge again when the sun shines and the sky becomes blue. Reality is getting up and going about household duties. Arising during skies of gray is difficult and so is going through difficult times or problems. If I just set my sight on the blue skies coming, I can anticipate instead of hibernate. Yesterday, I talked to a young woman. She had just come out of the drug scene. She had so many questions about God. I made sure to tell her in simple language that He loves her and He knows her name. What a sweet smile she gave me as she thanked me for taking time with her. She has come out of the storm and is walking in the sunshine. Her journey may be long but she's not alone. We are many and walk together, encouraging each other through the storms, which never last longer than we can bear.

## Pearl:

His words came together with meaning. He writes the thoughts and dreams, always thinking of what tomorrow holds and what yesterday brought. Dreams broken, sorrow and pain, yet his books and his music bring him joy. Now he sits and writes, slowly. He seems to be lost in thought. This talented and creative man is now at the mercy of meaningless smiles. He's lost in his world, in a world that no longer exists. All I remember of my brother is in my memory, forgotten by him. I sit by him and he smiles, his eyes staring blankly. He has left books of poetry to the next generation, thoughts written by a man of words. I'll never understand where that creative mind has gone. The disease that has become him is mysterious.

It attacks when least expected and just as fast, steals all that is and was of an intelligent mind.

<u>Life, a Miracle</u>
A life begins with innocence,
A pure heart, sweet smells
Sparkling eyes, pitiful cries,
Life, a miracle.

The innocence leaves,
Slowly slipping into the past,
Eyes wide open
Into life, running.

The running slows,
The clock is ticking.
Time stands still
Innocence looks back,

With smiling lips,
Glancing back, once more
Running into the future.
Once again, life, a miracle.

I am thinking today of generations of our family, each one living, dying, leaving their footprints behind. We walk ahead, leaving our footprints, leaving our heritage to go on, into the future.

## Patty:

When I remember my childhood, I realize I was raised with such a low self esteem. It followed me through college and then into ministry. I would come home and cry, because I couldn't seem to make friends easily. Way back then we were told not to have close friends within our congregation. Then as we did make friends, I saw how some were just superficial friends, loving us one day and leaving us and our church for the least little disagreement. When I told my husband that no one had talked to me Sunday or even shook my hand, he'd tell me to remember that people are people and they don't mean anything by it. Well, he doesn't understand that I need friends, I need people. I give and give of myself but sometimes it is still not enough. Years and years of short vacations and my husband studying even on Saturday, have left me and the children resenting the people who have taken our place in his life. I long for change in all of us, and a partially  normal life.

*Paige:*
　　Wow, where has time gone? The years fly by and you have taken my hand. You took care of me so our son could live. You drove me to the store when I couldn't drive. You showered us with gifts on our birthdays and holidays. You called and prayed for me on the phone. You adopted us into your families. You left groceries on our doorstep even as we were praying for God to supply our needs. Because of you we were able to take vacations we never dreamed of; by the sea; restful times to unwind. You sometimes clothed our children. You made it possible for us to purchase our first house. You took care of our children so we could get away to retreats and conferences, yet you would not let us pay you. You rocked and fed our crying, sleepy, hungry babies while I played the piano or sang in the choir. You put your arms around our teenagers and gave them love and care that they so needed. You were proud of them when they achieved in school and gave them compliments that meant so much to them. I think of the faces of ministry. I speak for thousands of women who belong to this special group, ministry wives, we in the parsonage, when I say thank you. I pray God will bless you as you have blessed us.

> Now I lay me down to sleep.
> I pray the Lord will your soul keep.
> As I lay my head to rest,
> May your life always be God blessed.

## Diane:

Times sure have changed since I was a preacher's kid. Now as a preacher's wife with my own children, I can hardly believe how I've seen the evolution of the church rules. When I was a teenager, as an only child, I probably was given privileges beyond my years. I realize now it made me an easy prey for the women with not much to do but look out for me. One Wednesday night, a church night, my parents said I could go to the school concert as I was in the Glee Club. As soon as my parents got to church, this trio of women ran to inform my father of his wayward daughter who was skipping church. How surprised they were when they were informed I was given permission by their pastor to actually go to an "ungodly" concert. I smiled at the memory as I drove our son to his ball game tonight and I skipped church to cheer him on. We've come a long way!

## Chrissy:

What a busy day! It snowed all day but not hard enough to be a blizzard. Today my husband had a funeral for a man who was old and forgotten in this life. Years ago he attended our church. Just last month we got a call from a neighbor of his telling us he wanted to see the pastor. My husband drove up to the apartment house where he lived. In a small room, he met Joe, in amidst filth and aged furniture. He saw Joe bent over, sitting in a chair and in dim light, the face and smell of an alcoholic. He had turned from God and family, yet had called for the pastor in his time of utter need and despair. My husband told him God still loved him and prayed for him. In finding Joe had no shoes; he went and bought him a pair. The tears in Joe's eyes showed his thankfulness. A few days later a call came again. Joe was in the hospital and dying. As my husband walked into the hospital room, Joe smiled and said, "Reverend, I've made my peace with God." In a couple of days the funeral director called and asked if my husband could do the service for Joe. My husband arrived, waited for an hour, and then realized that no one was coming to the funeral. Joe's family and friends had long forgotten him, as he had chosen a life without any of them. With tears in his eyes, my husband prayed over Joe's body, read scripture and thanked God that He had welcomed Joe to His heavenly home. Years of waste and loneliness had ended with Joe seeing his need of a loving God.

## Brenda:

She was the sweetest lady I have ever known. How could her husband hide this affair from her for so many years? Her life was full of grace, and many people admired her. Did she know or suspect that the woman who pretended to be her friend was little by little becoming closer and more attentive to her husband, the pastor? He, of course, ate up the attention and finally they were exposed. One more family is torn apart. One more church is thrown into a tailspin. He threw it all away for a life of deceit and short lived pleasure. His children are grown but now come to comfort their mother. He has lost their respect and now I heard that his lover has left him and he is already on to another woman again. I just can't understand how a man that has pastored many years can get up and preach the Bible to his congregation, knowing he is committing adultery. Does he have no conscience? Does he have no respect for his wife, his lover or himself? I guess not. He is deceived.

## Pauline:

Today our children were baptized in water. Because we do not have a baptismal tank in our church yet, we had the service at the lake. It was a beautiful day. The church had a picnic and then we all walked to the water. After several people were baptized, a lady walked into the water, was baptized, and then to everyone's surprise, she swam down the lake and out of sight. Another time, we had our baptismal service in a neighboring church. One man, who was quite tall, stood in the tank and gave a beautiful testimony. Then my husband began to baptize him, laying him back into the water, and to everyone's horror banged his head on the edge of the tank. Thank God he wasn't hurt. Funny things do happen, so I write them in my journal so our children will read them and see our years in the ministry and how we remember them, and have a laugh or two.

## Paige:

Feelings. Today has been a day of feelings. I think of the many years of ministry, different churches, different faces, yet all the same. The voices echo through the years; voices I hear like memories so far removed, yet so near. You say, "The pastor's wife is so stuck-up, or, she thinks she's above us." You didn't know how afraid I was of you and how young and immature I felt. I was your pastor's wife, but some of you could have been my mother or my grandmother. I could have used a little mothering now and then. You were upset because you tried to call us all day and we didn't answer until late that night. No cell phones back then. You didn't know how badly we needed the day off to walk along the water, talking with each other; just us two for one whole day, breathing together. Then how glad we were driving back home, refreshed, ready to give of ourselves to others again. We love to hear of your weekend to the

*108*      The Other Side of the Pulpit

shore or to the mountains, exciting trips. You say how "lucky" we are to go to our vacation to national church conventions with the church paying our way. If you could only know how I long to have a real vacation and let my hair down and not have to dress up and sit in hours of meetings and seminars. I enjoy going to them but they are a part of our ministry, not relaxing vacations. The burdens we carry as our husbands shepherd the flock sometimes makes us weary. Sometimes these burdens and heartaches kill our husbands prematurely. The devil attacks us and our families. If he gets us, it affects our church and community. But we are strong. We can't help but be. We are working for the King and He gives us strength. He dries our tears and holds us close. When we are distraught, He speaks peace. When we are lonely He is our friend. We have our spouses and our children but we also need you who are wives and mothers, just like us. Here's my hand, will you take it?

## *Carlotta:*
Today my friends and I went for a ride and lunch. We are so silly, always making up a story or mystery about people we see. So, we call ourselves *The Ladybugs*. We do have a lot of fun together.

<u>Ladybugs</u>
Ladybugs, ladybugs, where are you going?
Up to the mountains where the wind is blowing.
Up where a man lives, at the end of the way,
Hidden from people he knew yesterday.

We're solving a mystery and having such fun,
So now let's go quietly, one by one.
You peek in the windows; I'll crawl up the stairs,
If we're quiet enough, we'll go unawares.

Is he hiding a crime, does he have a gun?
If you hear some footsteps, just get up and run.
Maybe he's hiding from the law, or maybe hiding some money;
If he's hiding a body it sure won't be funny.

So we carefully try to solve the crime,
We ladybugs detectives three,
While the man in the house lets his dog outside,
And we hide in back of a tree.

The sun goes down, the lights go on,
Up in the house on the hill.
The ladybugs try to solve the crime,
But they cannot stand the chill.

So down to the car they run away,
With stories and clues in their heads;
Back to the pens and pencils,
And their own warm houses and beds.

*Irma:*
I can't believe the board in our church didn't think that my 50th High School reunion was important enough for my husband to take off a Sunday to drive and accompany me several states away. So we took it as part of our vacation time and enjoyed every minute of the weekend. So many memories revived.

<u>Yesterday</u>
Tell me where the years have gone,
It seems like yesterday,
When summer came with much delight,
And all we did was play.

Our parents knew the dates and times,
Of all the events of the year;
Our playmates were dolls and carriages,
We didn't have a care.

Was it really so long ago,
When we worried not a bit,
Of how much the groceries cost,
Or how many lights were lit?

We were so carefree and only cared
If our hair got messed in the breeze,
Or who we sat with on the bus,
And whom the boys would tease.

Why did the years go by so fast
When we were having such fun,
When girls giggled and whispered,
"He says I'm his only one."

We look at our pictures and reminisce,
And remember how excited we'd be,
At birthday or graduation parties,
How we felt so young and so free.

Now our children have left the nest,
As we did many years ago,
Now we go around shutting off lights,
We remind them to drive slow.

The aches and pains surround us,
Now we are getting old;
We are too hot in the summer,
Every winter is much too cold.

Now we go through the boxes
Read old letters with tears;
As we cherish the memories,
We've kept there through the years.

There for a few precious moments,
The years have melted away;
We run and laugh with no worries,
As we travel back to yesterday.

# CHAPTER 9

# SIMPLY TRUSTING

"It (love) does not rejoice about injustice but rejoices whenever the truth wins out. Love never gives up, never loses faith, is always hopeful, and endures through every circumstance" (1 Cor. 13:6-7).

# 9

## SIMPLY TRUSTING

---

*Elsa May:*
    Well, there you have it; so many feelings, so many glimpses into lives otherwise not heard from. Why do people write in journals? Perhaps they write to remember events, or to vent their feelings. Some write as prayers to God; a written prayer. I remember writing in a diary as a child and then as a teenager. Every night after writing, I would lock that diary with my little key. One day while reading the things that I had written from my young heart, I decided that I never wanted anyone to read it, so I threw the diary in the fireplace, burning my written memories. Now I wish that I had kept it so I could look back and see the girl I once knew: me.

    I have neglected writing in my own journal. Some of the stories in these journal entries have come from my own writings and some from the women I've met in 47 years of ministry. If you see yourself in these pages, be at peace and know you are not alone. Most of these stories have a happy ending; some do not. Nevertheless, God is always there to help carry the burdens. He always walks beside us, sometimes carrying us to ease our hurts and pain. The waters of life may be turbulent and sometimes calm. He is always there beside us. Please don't judge your pastor's wife by these journals. Instead, look at her and remember that she is a woman with feelings,

dreams, and screams, just like you. Do we fail God? Yes!
Does He ever fail us? No! I have learned that if I just
trust God, He will see me through every situation that
I face. That's the way it has been for me, on the other
side of the pulpit.

<u>Trust Me</u>
Childhood, nurtured by God's Word,
Sunday school, parties, free as a bird.
Friends, camps, rides and songs,
I trusted in Jesus all day long.

Teenage years, the tears, the fun,
The dark clouds came, but then the sun,
Until one sad day, my world stood still,
As my parents parted, I remember well,

The bitterness came and then the cold,
I felt in days I had grown so old;
But out of the dark, I could not see,
Came a voice so clear, "Trust Me."

I did not understand the way,
But God led me day by day.
On through school, then miles to go,
People to meet, I did not know,

All these things happening to me,
Were for the future I could not see.
It was then that the words would be,
So clear as He said, "Trust Me."

Out of the turbulent years away,
At a camp meeting on bended knee,
I questioned my future, what will it be?
God's gentle voice said, "Trust Me."

God's love, so true, His Word revealed,
Being fed and nurtured and being healed,
Yes, Bible school was a part of His will;
The plan was unfolding, I remember still.

One day Dave asked me to be his wife,
To love and to cherish the rest of my life.
Am I able to love and to share ministry?
Again came God's answer, "Trust Me."

Where shall we go, what shall we do?
Pennsylvania, New Jersey, Kalamazoo,
Vermont, oh Lord, can this really be?
We both heard it this time, "Trust Me."

We knew that God had sent us there,
Out of our love our son was born,
As I gazed at him that cold winter morn,
Wondering what his future would be,
I heard God again, "Trust Me."

Then again the path changed as we said goodbye,
And parted with friends and mountains so high,
God's hand was still there, as it always will be,
His voice was a whisper, "Trust Me."

Amid the victories, the struggles and strife,
A sweet little daughter was born in our life.
Oh God, You're so good, our hearts rise up to Thee,
Her dad takes her hand and says, "Trust Me."

I remember the morning Dave asked me to pray,
So I cried aloud, "Oh Lord have Your way,"
The tears and the waiting, now the victory was won,
As Dave smiled and said, "To Burlington."

The packing, the dear ones who had stood by our side,
Fed us and loved us and clothed us beside.
The words then came in a prophecy,
"You'll prosper and grow, it's My plan, trust Me."

Our life was so full; God gave us so much,
Healings, salvations, people to touch;
To help and to lead, new visions to see,
We understood why God had said, "Trust Me."

I remember the love He helped us to share,
How He filled up our home and taught us to care,
When our dear Juanita was taken to Heaven,
He lovingly sent us our little Paul and Kevin.

Growth and victories, struggles to meet,
Souls to lay at the Master's feet;
When our hearts were broken and we could not see,
Came the still small voice, "Oh please, trust Me."

Decisions to make, burdens to bear,
Around each corner, the devil's snare;
We're down at the bottom, we can't see,
God lifted us up with His tender, "Trust Me."

But how can I trust and how can I live?
I'm tired and discouraged; I don't want to give,
I've trusted and loved and can't You see,
I just can't hear You say, "Trust Me."

Into the darkness He reached His hand,
Stood us together in a new land;
A land with new visions, new love, we're not worthy,
But His voice comes much louder, "Now trust Me."

So we've trusted and grown amid laughter and tears,
Life so abundant, good friends, precious years;
All part of our life, yet now we must leave,
I'm sure the Lord understands as we grieve.

We come to another journey in life,
We travel together, this husband and wife;
It's a new journey, a new ministry,
Yet God's voice is so clear, "Trust Me."

"Trust in the LORD with all thine heart; and lean not unto thine own understanding. In all thy ways acknowledge him, and he shall direct thy paths" (Proverbs 3:5-6 , KJV).

# Ways You Can Help Your Pastor's Wife

Here are just a few of the *thousands* of ways you can help your pastor's wife.

1. Remember that the pastor and his wife are together, when you hurt one, you hurt the other.

2. Let her be who and what God has called her to be. Don't enforce your own expectations on her based on the previous pastor's wife or what you think she should do.

3. Don't get involved with the pastor family's private life; keep it private! (e.g., how they dress, what they do at home, their hobbies, how they discipline their children, etc.)

4. Don't expect the pastor's children to be examples just because they are pastor's kids. Remember they are children.

5. Only go in the pastor's home (church parsonage) when invited. Allow them the freedom to use electricity and heat how they choose to.

6. Pay her for work she does for the church. If the husband is the only income coming in for the family, the church hired them as a "package deal." If applicable, create a way to pay her so that she can have a work history, or release her to work a different career if she chooses to.

7. Bless her by treating her the way you would like to be treated. If there is an issue to discuss, do it in private, not in front of the whole congregation.

8. Show your gratitude to the *entire family* on Pastor Appreciation Sunday.

9. Pray for her and her family.

# About the Author

---

Elsa and her husband travel full time ministering to churches everywhere. They are seasoned ministers with a lot of valuable experience.

If you have related to the women in this book and have a story to tell the author, please email Elsa at:

naaanny90@aol.com

# More Titles by 5 Fold Media

**Favor, The Overlooked Ingredient for Success**
by Rhoda Banks
$8.00
ISBN: 978-0-9827980-1-0

*Favor, the Overlooked Ingredient for Success* gives a concise look at the various factors that cause us to advance. Although we have favor when we are born again, there are ways to increase and progressively grow in the favor of God.

In this booklet, you will learn the keys to unlocking favor and be challenged to seek the Lord for strategy on how to handle situations in order to gain ground.

**Deeper Relevance**
by Cheryl Stasinowsky
$21.00
ISBN: 978-0-9827980-8-9

Cheryl set out to write a daily encouraging word on her social networks, not realizing that her pursuit for a deeper understanding of God's Word would blossom into a full devotional.

Grab your Bible, along with this book, and get ready to discover Kingdom nuggets that will enrich your walk and relationship with Jesus. His Word truly sustains us every day!

# More Titles by 5 Fold Media

### A to Z Bible Stories
by Barbara Semple
$8.00
ISBN: 978-0-9825775-5-4

From the letter A through the letter Z, Barbara has illustrated stories that represent some of the main themes and characters in the Bible. As you read this book, you will gain a relationship and faith with the One who inspired them all: God.

Every decision we make is influenced by who and what we believe in. Shouldn't we begin early to teach our children the stories of faith?

### Spiritual Backpack
by Dr. Penny Waters
$11.00
ISBN: 978-0-9827980-0-3

Spiritual Backpack is a practical guide for understanding how to be prepared to handle unexpected situations.

Join Dr. Penny Waters as she reveals how common items found in a backpack can be associated with scriptural meaning. These quick and easy devotionals can be used privately or in a group setting.

Visit www.5foldmedia.com to sign up for **5 Fold Media's FREE email update.** You will get notices of our new releases, sales, and special events such as book signings and media conferences.

5 Fold Media, LLC is a Christ-centered media company. Our desire is to produce lasting fruit in writing, music, art, and creative gifts.

*"To Establish and Reveal"*
For more information visit:
**www.5foldmedia.com**

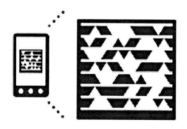

Use your mobile device to scan the tag above and visit our website. Get the free app: http://gettag.mobi

CPSIA information can be obtained at www.ICGtesting.com
Printed in the USA
BVOW012301070713

324831BV00007B/142/P